Rajput Miniatures from the Collection of Edwin Binney, 3rd

PORTLAND ART MUSEUM
Portland, Oregon
September 24 — October 20, 1968

FINE ARTS GALLERY OF SAN DIEGO
San Diego, California
October 29 — November 24, 1968

WILLIAM ROCKHILL NELSON GALLERY OF ART
ATKINS MUSEUM OF FINE ARTS
Kansas City, Missouri
December 5 — January 5, 1969

MUSEUM OF FINE ARTS
Boston, Massachusetts
January 15 — February 25, 1969

ART GALLERY OF GREATER VICTORIA
Victoria, B. C.
March 11 — March 30, 1969

SEATTLE ART MUSEUM
Seattle, Washington
April 10 — May 11, 1969

CALIFORNIA PALACE OF THE
LEGION OF HONOR
San Francisco, California
August 18 — September 21, 1969

HONOLULU ACADEMY OF ART
Honolulu, Hawaii
October 5 — November 2, 1969

TOLEDO MUSEUM OF ART
Toledo, Ohio
November 16 — December 14, 1969

RAJPUT MINIATURES

From the Collection of

Edwin Binney, 3rd

PORTLAND ART MUSEUM

Portland, Oregon

FOREWORD

One of the great satisfactions of museum work is the presentation of an exhibition that makes a genuine contribution to art historical studies and is at the same time aesthetically satisfying. Rajput Miniatures from the Collection of Edwin Binney, 3rd, is such an exhibition. It is also the first major showing of Rajput miniatures in some time; and it has been drawn entirely from a single private collection—a fact that is particularly remarkable in view of the richness and variety of the exhibition. Mr. Binney is a sensitive, knowledgeable, and tireless collector, and we find in his collection examples of all the schools of Rajput painting, with the Rajasthani states of Mewar, Bundi, and Kishangarh especially well represented. More significant still is the inclusion of much new material from the Punjab Hills: the many works from Kulu, Mankot, Mandi, Bilaspur, Nurpur, and Chamba are particularly important. The exhibition makes a pioneer contribution by bringing this material together, properly identifying it, and presenting it to the public in a number of American cities.

The fully illustrated catalog of the works included is a permanent addition to the literature in the field. Dr. W. G. Archer, D.Litt., Keeper, Indian Section, Victoria and Albert Museum, 1949-59, and presently Keeper Emeritus, a leading authority on the subject, has provided all the introductory chapters, and the identifications and attributions throughout are also his. Dr. Archer draws on an exceptional local knowledge of both Rajasthan and the Punjab Hills and, particularly with respect to the Punjab Hills, has presented new material and identified many schools for the first time. While preparing this catalog, Dr. Archer was also busy with his forthcoming major work, *Survey of Indian Paintings from the Punjab Hills,* to which we refer the reader who is interested in more detailed evidence on attributions than it is possible to present here.

The descriptions of individual works—the actual catalog entries—were written by Mr. Binney, whose intimate, personal knowledge of each miniature will be apparent to the reader at once.

The President and the Board of Trustees join me in expressing our warmest thanks to Mr. Binney, himself a Trustee of the Portland Art Association, for so generously lending this distinguished grouping from his collection; and to Dr. Archer for the keen insights and specialized knowledge he has brought to this undertaking.

FRANCIS J. NEWTON

INDIAN TEXTS REFERRED TO IN THE CATALOG

Baramasa
"The Twelve Months." A cycle of poems describing the behavior and feelings of lovers during each of the twelve months.

Bhagavata Purana
"The Ancient Story of God." A chronicle of Vishnu, the Loving Preserver, second member of the Hindu trinity, and of his avatars or incarnations. Books 10 and 11 describe the career on earth of his eighth incarnation, Krishna.

Chaurapanchasika
"Fifty Stanzas of Secret Love." A poem in Sanskrit by Bilhana (Kashmir, *fl.* 1100), celebrating a poet's intrigue with a king's daughter. Composed as if on the eve of his execution.

Gita Govinda
"The Song of the Herdsman." Poem in Sanskrit by Jayadeva (Bengal, *fl.* 1180-1200), recounting the loves of Radha and Krishna, their temporary estrangement and ultimate reconciliation.

Hamir Hath
"The Pride of Hamir." A ballad in Hindi describing the siege of Raja Hamir Dev in the fort of Ranthambhor by Ala-ud-din Khilji and his death from an arrow.

Kalpa Sutra
"The Sacred Aphorisms." A standard Jain text describing the careers of certain Jain saviors.

Kavi Priya
"The Poet's Breviary;" from *kavi*, "poet", and *priya*, "dear to" or "beloved by." A poem in Hindi by Keshava Das (Orchha, Bundelkhand, Central India, *fl.* 1580-1600), analysing different kinds of poetical effects and illustrating them with examples.

Laur Chanda
"The Romance of Lorik and the Lady Chandaini." A poem in Avadhi Hindi and Persian script by Maulana Daud (Oudh, Eastern India, 1380), describing the elopement of two lovers.

Nala Damayanti
An episode in the epic poem, the Mahabharata ("The Great [War of the] Bharatas"), describing the nuptials of Prince Nala and the Lady Damayanti, the loss of Nala's kingdom from gambling, and its eventual restoration.

Ragamala
"A Garland of Musical Modes." A cycle of poems apostrophising the princes *(ragas)* and ladies *(raginis)* who personify the spirits of the various melodies on which Indian music is improvised.

Ramayana
"The Adventures of Rama." An epic poem describing the exploits of Rama, seventh incarnation of Vishnu, in quest of his wife, Sita, abducted by Ravana, demon king of Ceylon. With the aid of bear and monkey allies, Rama overthrows Ravana and rescues Sita.

Rasamanjari
"A Posy of Delights." A poem in Sanskrit by Bhanu Datta (14th century) analysing varieties of lovers.

Rasika Priya
"The Lover's Breviary." A poem in Hindi by Keshav Das (see *Kavi Priya*) analysing lovers in terms of incidents involving Radha and Krishna.

Sat Saiya
"The Seven Centuries." A collection of seven hundred verses in Hindi by Bihari Lal (*fl.* 1650) celebrating the romance of Radha and Krishna.

Sursagar
"The Ocean of Sur Das." A series of poems in Hindi by Sur Das (*fl.* 1550) on the loves of Radha and Krishna.

Vanaparva (Aranyaka Parva)
"The Forest Section." Part of the epic poem, the *Mahabharata* (see Nala and Damayanti).

Introduction

When first used in the 20th century by the Indian art historian, Ananda Kentish Coomaraswamy, the term "Rajput Painting" had two distinct meanings. It was intended to refer to Indian miniatures of the 16th to 19th centuries which were un-Islamic in spirit and execution—to separate, that is, the foreign Mughal style of painting from a more national form of Indian expression. In the second place, it aimed at vindicating a type of art connected with a special group of non-Muslims, the soldierly Rajputs.

It was the Rajputs, Coomaraswamy believed, who had preserved Indian culture from the 13th to 16th centuries when much of India was overrun by alien Sultans from Central Asia. Rajput painting, therefore, had special virtues. "A vigorous archaic outline," he wrote, "is the basis of its language. Uncompromising, sensitive, reticent and tender, it lends itself to the utterance of serene passion and the expression of unmixed emotions." And he goes on, "It is no longer necessary to argue the distinction of Rajput from Mughal painting: for every addition to our knowledge makes it more evident that there could scarcely exist two contemporary schools more diverse in temper. Mughal art is at home in the portfolios of princely connoisseurs, whereas the Hindu paintings have stepped from the walls of palaces and public buildings. Mughal art is interested in individuality. It is not an idealization of life, but a refined and accomplished representation of a very magnificent phase of it. It is dramatic, splendid and attractive, but it rarely touches the deep springs of life. Its greatest successes are achieved in portraiture and in the representation of courtly pomp and pageantry. Its subject matter is of purely aristocratic interest; while that of the Rajput painters is universal. The distinction of Mughal from Rajput painting is nowhere more apparent than in the fact that the former is aristocratic and professional, while the latter is hieratic and popular and often essentially mystic." And he concludes, "Mughal art, however magnificent its brief achievement, was but an episode in the long history of Indian painting: Rajput painting belongs to the main stream."

Such a view was salutary when this great critic wrote, for, in 1916, Mughal painting had a virtual monopoly of aesthetic attention. But it was too extreme to survive.

Indeed as we survey the painting of Rajasthan, Central India, and the Punjab Hills—
the three parts of northern India which are most firmly connected with Rajput painting
—we realize that almost every statement Coomaraswamy so smoothly adumbrated
needs modification. Rajput painting is not popular, but is as aristocratic as Mughal.
It frequently revels in the courtly routine of a feudal nobility, records scenes of
hunting and celebrates one proud visage after another. Like Mughal miniatures, it is
often concerned with the poetry of music (*Ragamalas,* or "Garlands of Tunes"). Not
all Rajput miniatures have vigorous outlines; neither is all Rajput art tender, reticent,
and serene. Certain Rajput pictures have a barbaric intensity; others are graceful,
sophisticated, and elegant. Rajput painters were not amateurs but professionals. Rajput
paintings are not at all a contraction of murals, but are themselves the prototypes of
many wall paintings. Finally, on grounds of style, much more subtle distinctions must
now be made. Far from belonging to a single "main stream," Rajput miniatures
developed in two distinct ways and include two separate and contrasting manners.

The first Rajput style is a Rajput adaptation of an early Indian mode of bold
distortion which may originally have been derived from primitive village paintings
(often, but incorrectly, called "folk art"). The style was first employed in a sophisticated
manner in the 13th century for the Jains of western India — a business community
with an ascetic, puritanical religion. Later, in the 15th and 16th centuries, the Jain
style was applied to other subjects and was enlarged and transformed under the
stimulus of various Sultanate rulers. These had cultural connections with Persia, itself
the possessor of a highly delicate miniature art. It was therefore under Muslim pressures
that the first and earliest style of Rajput painting evolved. This early style was
distinguished by lack of realism, a hieratic treatment of human figures, a preference for
schematic symbols, and by a frequent recourse to flat expanses of glowing color.
It distorted faces, figures, trees, and architecture; and in its general approach to form
and color displayed the same daring as is typical of modern art. Its aim was to
parallel certain qualities which were valued in Rajput life and thought—virile ardour,
uncompromising bravery, independence, and romantic freedom. It emphasized

expression rather than beauty and, as a consequence, women in early Rajput miniatures are often as "unbeautiful" as those in pictures by Picasso or Miro. It followed that this first Rajput style was the opposite of Mughal; yet, by a paradox which shows how hard it is to frame convincing distinctions, some of the first Rajput painters were Muslims.

The second style is an adjustment to Rajput conditions of Mughal painting itself. During the crucial years 1560 to 1600, when Mughal painting was in process of evolution, the Mughal Emperor Akbar (1556-1605) turned to Indian painters to interpret his very personal requirements. A new style was invented, marked by delicate realism and representational finesse. It aimed at recording great events—mythical, historical, or contemporary. Indeed its purpose was often to perpetuate moments of crisis in the manner of a modern newsreel. Under the emperor Jahangir (1605-27) it magnified the sovereign and even interpreted him as an almost cosmological phenomenon. Later still, it recorded scenes of courtly life, including dalliance. For conveying a greater sense of illusion, it employed devices such as shading and perspective. Color was also used in a literal rather than a symbolic manner.

This style of sensitive naturalism stood in sharp contrast to its immediate Indian predecessors, but there are two circumstances which may explain its sudden emergence. Its patron, Akbar, had a zestful appreciation of Indian life and a desire to project his own personality. Indian artists, on their side, were willing to discard their former styles and accept new models. These were at hand in the more naturalistic art of Safavid Persia and in the Flemish and Italian engravings, miniatures, and Books of Hours which had begun to reach the Mughal court through European adventurers and missionaries. Two kinds of foreign painting, each in line with Akbar's taste, were therefore available, and it was by studying their techniques and then adjusting them to Indian subjects that Indian artists at the imperial court developed Mughal painting.

Rajput rulers may, at first, have resisted this new development; not only did it break with previous Indian conventions but its close link with a new non-Rajput imperial power discouraged quick adoption. Yet, despite initial dislike, Rajput hostility to the Mughals weakened. Rajput princesses joined the imperial harem; Rajput princes served in the imperial forces; Mughal court life proved on examination to be not so very different from Rajput. Above all, certain aspects of Rajput religion and culture favored the replacement of the early brusque manner by a style of tender refinement.

In Rajput states, Vishnu the Loving Preserver, Shiva the Destroyer and Procreator, and Devi, his female counterpart, had long been worshipped. During the 12th century, however, a new religious movement had grown up in western and eastern India. In contrast to salvation by means of *dharma* or "right living"—the faithful performance of conventional duty—*bhakti* or salvation through love or devotion was fervently advocated. Rama, whose earthly career as the seventh incarnation of Vishnu was recounted in an epic, the *Ramayana,* had personified the moral ideal. Krishna, the eighth incarnation of Vishnu, reflected a new conception. His romance with a married milkmaid, Radha, had been described in a long text of about the 10th century, the *Bhagavata Purana,* in which, however, Radha's name had been carefully suppressed. At the end of the 12th century, the Bengali poet, Jayadeva, boldly named her as Krishna's supreme love; and his long poem, the *Gita Govinda,* encouraged other poets to treat her and Krishna as ideal types. Striking examples of such poetry were the *Rasika Priya* of Keshav Das, written in 1592, and the *Sat Saiya* of Bihari Lal, written in 1662.

For Rajputs, this poetry had three functions. It expressed devotion to God by praising Krishna; it provided a vivid allegory of divine union (Radha in ignoring conventional morals was the soul leaving all for love of God); and it emphasized the traditional Indian need for romantic love. In ancient India, relations between the sexes had often approximated in freedom to those in modern Western society. By the Indian Middle Ages, this freedom had been eroded, marriages had tended to become mere social alliances, ladies were secluded, and hence, for Rajput princes and their courtiers, romance was often possible only with dancing girls or courtesans. The cult of Krishna vindicated romantic love and by being publicly extolled in poetry, assuaged needs which might otherwise have been repressed. In all this poetry, woman was regarded as a source of rapture and enchantment. Tender and devoted, she was also courtly and refined. It is no surprise that in poems about Radha, the milkmaid was treated as if she were a princess. The setting might be the woods; the atmosphere was that of a palace.

Poetry of this sort, at once devotional and romantic, had existed in the mid-16th century, but it is difficult to regard the first style of Rajput painting, with its brusque distortions, as providing an adequate equivalent. In the 5th century, the love poetry of Kalidasa had been matched by the murals of Ajanta, where supple beauties were rendered with graceful naturalism. A style of precisely this kind was needed in order to express the sensuous elements in Rajput culture. By the 17th century, Mughal painting was ready to provide it. Due, therefore, to the growing appeal of the Radha-Krishna cult and an added interest in courtly love, painters at certain Rajput courts adopted Mughal conventions and, in the course of the 17th and 18th centuries, adjusted them to Rajput needs.

The result of their experiments was the second style of Rajput painting, as delicate in character as the first had been robust. Lively naturalism, the recreation of physical charm, and a complete repudiation of the "unbeautiful" were now as much Rajput characteristics as had been the previous savage vitality. At certain courts, rhythmical simplification was still favored, and color was, at times, used symbolically. The need for refinement, however, was unchallenged and, in these exquisite pictures, courtly elegance, romantic passion, and sensuous devotion were paralleled by grace of style.

It is these two modes of expression, each vitally Rajput yet each in sharp contrast to the other, which give Rajput miniatures their complex richness and infuse the present exhibition with such glowing brilliance.

W. G. ARCHER

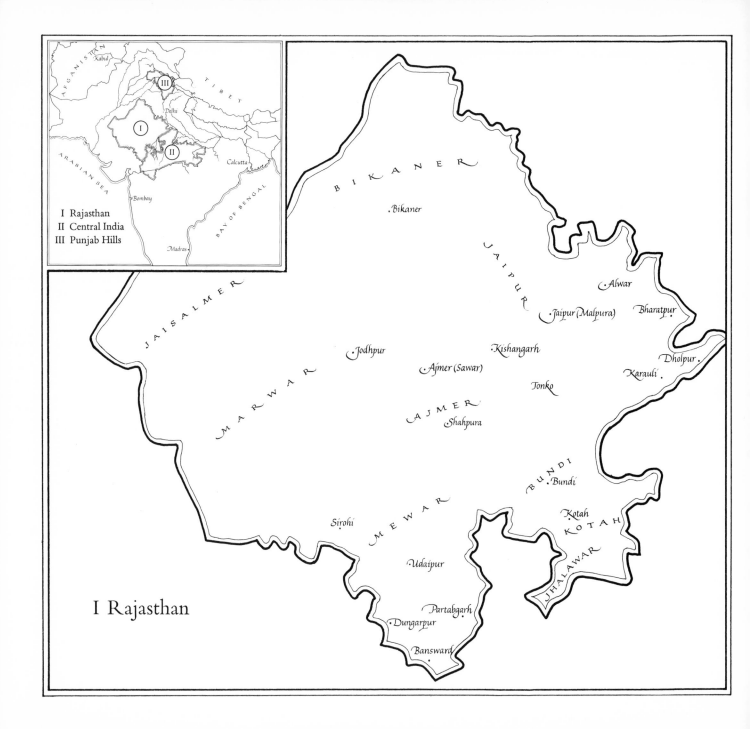

I Rajasthan
II Central India
III Punjab Hills

I Rajasthan

I Rajasthan

From the 16th to 19th centuries, Rajasthan or "Rajputana" included twenty feudal states. Poised like a blunt diamond in the heart of Northern India, it was a tract of country 500 miles long by 450 miles wide. In its lower half, a range of mountains ran up from southwest to northeast, separating the desert states of Jaisalmer, Marwar and Bikaner on the west from the jungle-covered states of Mewar, Bundi and Kotah on the southeast. In the upper half, the hills dwindled, the large state of Jaipur to the east forming a continuation of Bikaner. Out of a total of twenty states, two—Dholpur and Bharatpur on the extreme east—were ruled by Jats, a non-Rajput community of the Punjab; and a third, Tonk, was a collection of Muslim enclaves. Seventeen states were wholly Rajput, but of these only six were both large and important. Of the remaining eleven, Alwar and Karauli acted as easterly buffers between Jaipur and the Mughal provinces of Agra and Delhi. Sirohi, Partabgarh, Banswara and Dungarpur were petty adjuncts of Mewar in the south. Jhalalwar was a tiny strip at the southern end of Kotah. Ajmer, Kishangarh and Shahpura formed a small compact group in the center. Jaisalmer was a desert state too far to the west to influence events. The six states of greatest significance were Mewar, Bundi, Kotah, Marwar, Bikaner and Jaipur.

MEWAR

The first proof of painting in Mewar—premier state of Rajasthan and chief defender of Rajput culture—is a *Ragamala* series (no. 2) painted in 1605 by a Muslim painter Nasir-ud-din, at Chawand, temporary capital of Mewar from 1576 to 1615. The series has black, red, and dark green backgrounds, bands of white on the skyline, figures with staring eyes and margins painted in a special shade of sunny yellow. These primitive idioms also occur in a *Bhagavata Purana* (no. 1 a-c) and a *Gita Govinda* (Prince of Wales Museum, Bombay), and despite minor differences of detail, it seems clear that all three sets must belong to the same local tradition. It is significant that unlike the *Ragamala,* the last two are highly devotional in character and are thus especially relevant to Mewar where the cult of Krishna had already won strong support. The antecedents of this Mewar style were almost certainly at Mandu, capital of Malwa in Central India (q.v.). There, two related series —a *Laur Chanda* and a *Chaurapanchasika*—were probably executed in about 1550 for a Muslim prince, Baz Bahadur, and his Hindu mistress, the courtesan Rupmati. When, in 1561, Baz Bahadur was defeated by the Mughals, local painters may have been dispersed, some of them going to the wilds of Mewar where they could well have founded a new school. Although dependent in style on the *Laur Chanda* and the *Chaurapanchasika,* the *Bhagavata Purana* (no. 1 a-c) and the *Gita Govinda* are clearly different in prevailing mood and spirit and can therefore be reasonably connected with a different, though neighboring, court and culture. In this view, the *Bhagavata Purana* was painted in Mewar in about 1565 shortly after the painters' arrival and the *Gita Govinda* somewhat later, perhaps in 1580. It is of interest that the *Gita Govinda* was actually found there.

The forty years from 1565 to 1605 saw the growth from Malwa origins of a distinctive Mewar style; in the next fifty years this Mewar style reached luxuriant maturity. Until 1628, when Rana Jagat Singh I (1628-52) came to the throne, the Chawand artist, Nasir-ud-din, may himself have played a vital role in developing this early manner, and to him or one of his associates may perhaps be ascribed an early *Rasika Priya* of about the year 1615 (no. 3). Here the standard facial idioms of later Mewar painting are still evolving, the lushly flowering trees of the *Gita Govinda* are still assertive, and male figures continue to wear an early type of coat with pointed ends. From 1628 onwards, the output of Mewar painting is greatly accelerated, and it is likely that the new Rana, Jagat Singh I, provided the crucial incentive. A *Ragamala* dated 1628 by a new painter, Shahab-ud-din—a Muslim like Nasir-ud-din and perhaps a member of the same artist family—ushers in this new period, and twenty years later there is a glut of dated manuscripts, four of them by Shahab-ud-din himself (dated 1648, 1650, 1652 and 1655), one of them by a Hindu painter Manohar (1649), and yet another by an unnamed painter working at the resurrected fortress of Chitor in 1651. Between 1628 and 1648 Shahab-ud-din and his colleagues can hardly have sat idle, and to this period, part, at least, of the vast Mewar output must be ascribed. Of these three master painters, Shahab-ud-din appears to have commanded the most fluent and lively style, Manohar the most rational, and the unnamed painter of the 1651 Chitor series the most robust and glamorous. His hand is evident in a *Sursagar* series in the Kanoria collection, Calcutta, and he or his assistants must also be credited with illustrations to the *Rasika Priya,* the "Gem Palace" *Ragamala* (National Museum, New Delhi), a *Kavi Priya* (no. 5), and a series of illustrations to an unidentified text (no. 4 a-c). In these pictures the early fondness for red and black backgrounds is maintained but the picture space has been greatly enlarged. Four roughly equal rectangular compartments are employed and within this loosely geometrical scheme, eager figures with sharp robust forms and keen intent eyes re-enact the careers of Rama and Krishna, the ways of ideal lovers (no. 3), and even the adventures of princes in search of a Jain teacher (no. 4 c). The maintenance of the "single plane" convention and a firm rejection of modelling allows each shape to make the maximum impact, and the deployment of glowing reds, blues, browns, greens, and oranges evokes a mood of ardent elation.

Between 1652 and 1752 under Ranas Raj Singh, Jai Singh, Amar Singh II, Sangram Singh, and Jagat Singh II, large illustrated sets continued to be produced. Their subjects included Persian proverbs, a book of good and bad omens, fables, the story of Krishna and Rukmini, a Book of Dreams (no. 7), the *Sat Saiya* of the poet Bihari (no. 8) and yet further examples of the *Ramayana* and *Bhagavata Purana* (no. 9). The lyrical fervor and passionate intensity of the Jagat Singh I period (1628-52) seems, however, to have slackened; and while the early zest for strong color remains, compositions become somewhat sparser, figures less lively and faces more staid. Contemporary with this slackening of vigor, new influences become apparent. In a *Ragamala* of about 1685 (shared by the Cleveland and Boston Museums), the male figure impersonating the *Raga* seems clearly modelled on the young Amar Singh II as prince. A portrait of him (no. 6) of about 1700 shows him after his accession and it is obvious that Mughal influence of a new kind has now intervened. Both the Rana and his companions are shown in pale colors with shaded figures; there is a marked interest in individual character, and this is even extended to include favorite horses and elephants. A portrait of an elephant dated 1699 in the Khajanchi collection is inscribed with the elephant's name, Jayamangal, and there are many other studies which evince the same lively concern. These animal portraits are clearly based on direct observation, and it is significant that the winged elephants in the Book of Dreams (no. 7) already have a naturalistic flavor and share the elephant Jayamangal's markings.

This concentration on the Rana and his animals is symptomatic of developments at Mewar in the 18th and 19th centuries. Although the painting of religious texts was not entirely abandoned it tended to become a stale repetition of 17th century models. In contrast, a crude but lively style of journalistic reporting grew up and under Amar Singh II's successors, painting focused on the activities of the ruler, his feudal progresses, courtly amusements, and royal hunts. In 1954 the palace at Udaipur still contained heaps of giant pictures, often measuring three feet by five, showing in panoramic detail Mewar rulers journeying through the countryside.

Such grandiose celebrations of the Rana do not seem to have outlasted the 18th century, but two pictures in the Victoria and Albert Museum—one dated 1835 showing Rana Jawan Singh (1828-38) on horseback slashing at a boar, the other dated 1855 depicting Rana Sarup Singh (1842-61) shooting boars from the howdah of an elephant—testify to the same obsessive interest. A picture of Gokul Das chasing a boar with its litter (no. 10) confirms the special place that boar hunting held in Mewar life. In both the dated pictures not only is the landscape green but the hunters are clad in green dresses. In the latter picture, however, the green of the background is a crude arsenic—in screaming contrast to the rich coloring which had given Mewar painting its glowing radiance two centuries before.

1 Three leaves from a *Bhagavata Purana* series.

c. 1560-65

approximately 7 x 9¼

a) THE CATTLE AND COWHERD CHILDREN LEAVE THE CAVE

The god Brahma, to tease Krishna, has imprisoned the cattle and some of the cowherd children in a cave. Krishna has arranged their liberation, and they are shown leaving the cave in the lower right portion of the miniature.

b) KRISHNA IN THE JAWS OF THE DEMON AGRASURA

The young Krishna early displayed unusual powers (thus revealing his divine origin) by protecting his young companions and their herds from various evil-doers, such as the river snake Kaliya (nos. 70 and 97) and the giant crane Bakasura (no. 94). Here, the might of Agrasura is suggested by the size of his coils which start in the upper right corner, under the inscription, and proceed counterclockwise around the miniature to the huge head where Krishna is shown holding the demon's jaws open to allow the escape of the cows and their young herders. The three men in the lower right are so impressed by the young Krishna's feat that they join their hands in a gesture of respectful wonder.

c) THE ATTACK ON THE CITADEL OF NARAKASURA

The demon Naraka sits on a throne in his castle, surrounded by courtiers. In another room (above) are seated two of the captive Gandharva and Apsaras women whom he has imprisoned. The impregnability of the citadel is suggested by the wide moat and the girdle of cannon which surround it. Krishna and his wife Satyabhama arrive to destroy Naraka for his abductions and for the theft of a pair of heavenly earrings. Krishna carries a discus, a sword, a lotus, and a conch shell, all attributes of the god Vishnu of whom he is an avatar. He is borne aloft by the man-bird Garuda, Vishnu's usual mount (see no. 15). Krishna will shortly kill Naraka with his discus, recover the missing earrings, free the captive girls and rifle the treasury of the demon king. He will then continue on his celestial journey to Indra's capital.

1a THE CATTLE AND COWHERD CHILDREN LEAVE THE CAVE
Mewar

1b KRISHNA IN THE JAWS OF THE DEMON AGRASURA
Mewar

(A leaf reproduced in the Heeramaneck catalog —see below—shows the continuation of the journey of Krishna on Garuda.)

Other leaves from this series have been reproduced. See Khajanchi catalog, pl. A and 20; Lee, pp. 14 and 15; Welch and Beach, no. 3 a and b (which gives an incomplete list of some of the other owners of leaves from the series); Craven, no. 31 a; Heeramaneck catalog, p. 101 (this catalogs additional owners); and the McNear catalog, no. 7.

There are also unpublished leaves in the British Museum, London; Bharat Kala Bhavan, Banaras; and the Archer collection.

1C THE ATTACK ON THE CITADEL OF NARAKASURA   Mewar

श्रीप्रत्यनिकायथा॥प्रालोश्वरकिमपिज्रत्यविनिर्गमायत्नामोदरीव
दनैंमयांचका राःश्रालीउनर्निजितमेत्यलतानिकुंजशुम्नवकोकि
लधनिसात्तान

3   THE RETURN
OF THE HUSBAND
Mewar
Catalog page 19

Color Plate Section

Catalog resumes on page 18

20a KRISHNA KNOCKS ON
THE PALACE OF RADHA
Kotah
Catalog page 34

7

25 A LADY SEATED
ON A RAISED COUCH
IS ATTENDED
BY HER TWO MAIDS
Kishangarh
Catalog page 41

48 KRISHNA DANCES
WITH THE COWGIRLS
Narsinghgarh, Malwa
Catalog page 63

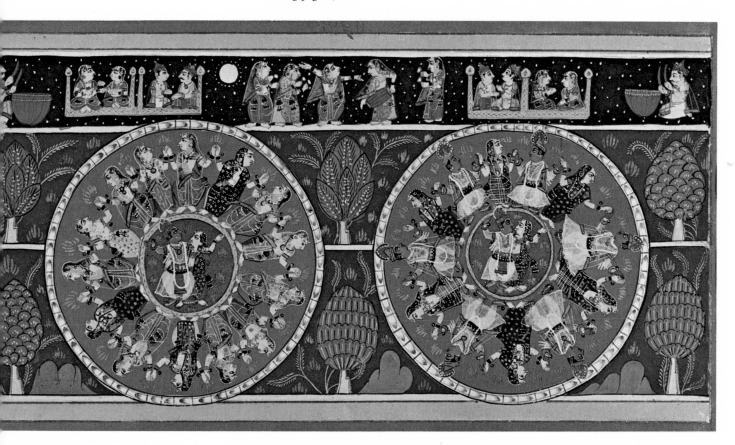

49 THE CONFIDANTE OF USHA,
    DAUGHTER OF THE DEMON KING VANASURA,
    CARRIES THE SLEEPING ANIRUDDHA,
    GRANDSON OF KRISHNA, TO HER MISTRESS
    Nepal
    Catalog page 64

70a PUNYAKI RAGINI,
WIFE OF BHAIRAVA RAGA
Bilaspur
Catalog page 92

82   THE FISH INCARNATION OF VISHNU
KILLING THE DEMON HAYAGRIVA
Chamba
Catalog page 107

87 RADHA AND KRISHNA
ON A HILLTOP
Garhwal
Catalog page 113

92b KRISHNA AWAITS ANXIOU
TO HEAR OF THE SUCCESS
OF HIS EMISSARY TO RAD
Kangra
Catalog page 121

2 KHAMBAVATI RAGINI   Mewar, Chawand

बाड़ीबसानामरदछछुछं कुत्राबदातीचउरानस्या बिरंचबेदोप
कमंसिका बेलावतालछ्यविवि ऋऐवा ॥८॥

छंबाईबीरागिनि

2 KHAMBAVATI RAGINI From a *Ragamala* series.
Chawand, dated 1605

$7\frac{3}{4}$ x $7\frac{1}{2}$

An inscription at the base of another leaf in this
series, the *Maru Ragini* in the Kanoria collection,
Calcutta, is dated samvat year 1662 (1605 A.D.).
The inscription names Nisaradi (Nasir-ud-din),
a Muslim, as the painter and the village of
Chauda (Chawand) as the place where it was
painted. At the beginning of the 17th century,
Chawand was the temporary capital of Mewar,
the major city of Chitor having been destroyed
by the troops of the Mughal Emperor Akbar,
and Udai Singh's new capital, Udaipur, being
still "a collection of huts."

Leaves from this series, in other collections,
have been reproduced in Archer (1957 a), no. 18,
pl. I, and *Indian Miniatures,* pl. 38; Kanoria catalog
(1957), pl. 1–3; Khajanchi catalog, no. 22,
fig. 31; Lee, no. 13, p. 24; Barrett and Gray,
p. 132; Welch and Beach, no. 7, p. 58; and
Heeramaneck catalog, no. 147, p. 123.
Unpublished leaves are in the Victoria and
Albert Museum, London; Bharat Kala Bhavan,
Banaras; the Archer collection, London, and the
Kanoria and Goenka collections, Calcutta.

3 THE RETURN OF THE HUSBAND From a
Rasika Priya series.

c. 1615

9¾ x 7½

The square treatment of the somewhat earlier
Chawand *Ragamala* of 1605 (no. 2) is here
multiplied in several boxlike shapes. The man
and woman in the room on the left with its flat
red background are lifted above the larger
square on the right. This larger box is marked
by an equally bright orange background which
is hardly obscured by the decorative tendrils of
the tree in which the second lady sits. The
principal male figure is wearing a transparent
four-pointed skirt *(jama)*. This fashion, which
was probably current in South Rajasthan and
Central and Eastern India (Jaunpur) from the
early 16th century on into part of the
17th, was adopted by the Emperor Akbar
during his initial period of "Indianizing."

Leaves from this series, in other collections, are
reproduced in Archer (1957 a), no. 24, pl. VIII;
Chandra, *Mewar*, pl. 1; and Lee, no. 14, p. 25.
Unpublished leaves are in the National Museum,
New Delhi; Bharat Kala Bhavan, Banaras; and
the Kanoria collection, Calcutta.

4a

4b

4c

4 Three leaves illustrating an unidentified text.

c. 1635-45

6¼ x 10½

a) Upper register:

A NOBLE CONVERSING WITH A LADY

Lower register:

TWO NOBLES DUELING WITH SWORD
AND SHIELD

b) Upper register:

A NAKED ASCETIC AND A DISCIPLE PREPARE
COSMETICS BEFORE A SEATED LADY

Lower register:

A NOBLE SEATED IN A SWING IS PRESENTED
WITH A PLATE OF FOOD

c) Single register:

A JAIN TEACHER RECEIVES A PRINCE AND
HIS RETINUE

In style, these leaves are similar to the "Gem
Palace" *Ragamala* (National Museum, New
Delhi) and the *Sursagar* (Kanoria collection,
Calcutta), both of which are probably by the
unnamed master of a *Ramayana* executed at
Chitor in 1651. The naked figure, receiving the
prince, is a member of the Jain Digambara sect,
which believed that nudity was sacred. The
chief adherents of Jainism were members of the
merchant and trading classes, many of whom
originally came from Gujarat (Western India)
and South Rajasthan.

Other leaves from this series, of which none
has so far been reproduced, are in the Binney
and Heeramaneck collections.

5 KRISHNA DISMISSED From a *Kavi Priya* series.

c. 1635-45

9¼ x 7½ (within border)

The wavy line of the banana tree and pillar of
the porch in this picture relieve the stark
division into compartments seen in nos. 2
and 3. Colors, however, are similar to those of
previous examples.

Other leaves from this *Kavi Priya* series are in
the collections of Dr. Leland C. Wyman,
Jamaica Plain, Massachusetts; and Mr. and Mrs.
Charles Page, John Yeon, and other private
collectors of the West Coast.

Upper register:
NOBLE CONVERSING WITH A LADY
Lower register:
TWO NOBLES DUELING WITH SWORD AND SHIELD
war
Upper register: A NAKED ASCETIC AND
A DISCIPLE PREPARE COSMETICS BEFORE A SEATED LADY
Lower register:
NOBLE SEATED IN A SWING
PRESENTED WITH A PLATE OF FOOD
war
A JAIN TEACHER RECEIVES A PRINCE AND HIS RETINUE
war

5 KRISHNA DISMISSED
Mewar

Episode from a *Book of Dreams*
c. 1720

10 x 8¼

It is not surprising in a country where the elephant provided a means both of royal transport and of heavy labor, to find it serving as the basis for an imaginary beast such as we see in this painting. The griffin and phoenix, legendary animals used in medieval European lore, had, in a similar fashion, their basis in more familiar animals.

7 WINGED ELEPHANTS IN A LANDSCAPE   Mewar

6 PORTRAIT OF RANA AMAR SINGH II OF MEWAR
Mewar

6 PORTRAIT OF RANA AMAR SINGH II OF MEWAR
(ruled 1698–1710)
Drawing with washes of color and gold.
c. 1700

9⅛ x 7⅛

The use of a halo around the head of a reigning prince was adopted from Mughal painting, which had taken it over from pictures of European saints.

Other similar portraits of Rana Amar Singh II are reproduced in Welch and Beach, no. 28, p. 73 (where he is on horseback) and in Skelton, no. 10 (where he is lying on a couch surrounded by attendants).

8 KRISHNA TALKS TO TWO COWGIRLS
(upper right)
WHILE RADHA IS CONSOLED BY
THREE COMPANIONS
(lower left)
Mewar

8 KRISHNA TALKS TO TWO COWGIRLS (upper right)
WHILE RADHA IS CONSOLED BY THREE
COMPANIONS (lower left)
From a *Sat Saiya* series.
c. 1720
$9^7/_8$ x $8^{11}/_{16}$

Again the Mewar square boxes, this time
separated by more sparse vegetation. Pictures
from this state have already used the more
horizontal format and will in the future (see
no. 9), but the convention of the square
compartments still continues. The human
figures, however, are more squat.
The *Sat Saiya* (1662) by the poet Bihari Lal is
another of the many Hindu literary works
which feature the life of Krishna and his
adventures among the cowgirls.

Other leaves from the same series are reproduced
in Welch and Beach, no. 37 a and b.

9 KRISHNA PLAYS WITH A COBRA WHILE BALARAMA
TRIES TO STEAL A SWORD
From a *Bhagavata Purana* series
c. 1750
9 x 14⅞ (within borders)
Exhibited: Persian and Indian Miniatures,
Binney Collection, Portland Supplementary
Exhibition. Cat. no. 55 a (incorrectly attributed
to Malwa).

The baby Krishna, painted blue, as he is an
avatar or incarnation of Vishnu, plays with his
half-brother Balarama who is white skinned.
Vishnu, "the Preserver," a god who was early
associated with the sun, appears on the cosmic
ocean at the beginning of each era. It is natural
that blue is his color, and also the hue of his
human avatars, Rama and Krishna.

The compartments are still present, but the
room at the left is the only square one. Another
Mewar convention is seen in the foliage of the
tree at the extreme right, with its plain hive-
like mass overpainted with five-finger shapes in
different colors.

9 KRISHNA PLAYS WITH A COBRA WHILE BALARAMA TRIES TO STEAL A SWORD Mewar

10 GOKUL DAS
HUNTING BOAR
Mewar

10 GOKUL DAS HUNTING BOAR
c. 1820-50
6½ x 9⅛ (within borders)
Exhibited: Persian and Indian Miniatures,
Binney Collection, Portland Supplementary
Exhibition. Cat. no. 77 a.
Inscribed in *nagari* characters: *sri gokal das ji.*
One of the favorite pastimes of the Rajput
prince or noble was hunting. Boars were kept
in a state park near Udaipur, capital of Mewar,
and a boar hunt was an important part of the
lavish festival held each spring in honor of the
goddess Gauri.

The nobleman pictured here wears a band
under his chin which holds his turban on his
head during the chase. The festoon of flowers
attached to the horse's mane suggests the
festivities of the annual boar hunt. The hunter's
lance crosses the curved line of the dog and the
family of boar. The painting is very coarse, the
landscape suggested by the most rudimentary
of lines below.

BUNDI

Painting in Bundi, a state in southeast Rajasthan, falls into four distinct phases, each of which can be connected with the person and character of a particular Bundi ruler. Until the lifetime of Rao Chattar Sal (reigned 1631-59) there is no evidence that any painting was practiced in Bundi—perhaps the earliest precursor of a local style being a *Ragamala* series with Jahangiri features illustrated by Pramod Chandra (1959), Barrett (1963) and Welch and Beach (1965). This series has been dated 1590 on the strength of a Persian inscription which, besides giving this date, further claims that it was produced by two Muslim painters associated with Mir Sayyid Ali and Abdus Samad. These latter artists were the Persian masters who founded the early Akbar school of Mughal painting. It is possible, however, that so flamboyant an inscription is spurious. Pending further investigation, therefore, it seems wiser to take a more sober view and to date the series about 1625. This date precedes by six years the actual accession of Chattar Sal, but his association as a prince with the future emperor Shah Jahan, as well as the stimulating proximity of Mewar, could well explain the appearance of artists at the Bundi court.

From 1630 onwards a distinctive Bundi style begins to develop, concentrating partly on the portrayal of Chattar Sal and his ladies and partly on further illustrations of the poetry of music (no. 11). In some of these latter pictures the lover's features are clearly based on those of Chattar Sal himself. In Rajput states, artists often treated members of the ruling house as models of masculine charm, and at Bundi this was to prove a standard practice until the 19th century. Under Bhao Singh (1659-81) *Ragamala* subjects and scenes of courtly life continued to be popular, but further themes—the *Rasika Priya* of Keshav Das (no. 14 a-b), and the love adventures of Krishna—were also included. Bhao Singh replaced his father, Chattar Sal (no. 12) as the current prototype of handsome lovers and in an elaborate picture (illustrated Welch and Beach, 1965) the process of substitution goes even further. He now appears seated with various beauties of the court, his own features strikingly matched by those of his ladies. The same courtly homage is tendered in a *Ragamala* picture (no. 11) and a *Rasika Priya* (nos. 14 a-b) where both male and female faces are again modelled on Bhao Singh's features. Such pictures of about the years 1670 to 1680, with their golden yellows and royal blues, brilliant greens and glowing scarlet, evoke a fantasy world of innocent enchantment. Brahminy ducks, traditional symbols of devoted lovers, sport in the pools; ladies with neat figures and piquant faces stroll in lush groves and even the hillsides are studded with flowering trees as if Nature herself were abetting the quest for love.

Until 1700 this ardent and poetic style characterized Bundi painting. By 1689, however, a slight coarseness has already developed and in a picture of that year, "the gift of the painter, Mohan," a prince stands with a lady on a footstool gazing at the new moon. They are surrounded by trees laden with heavy blossoms, but although

11 HINDOLA RAGA Bundi

11 HINDOLA RAGA From a *Ragamala* series.
Drawing with spots of color.
c. 1635-40
9⅜ x 6¼
Hindola Raga, "the swing music," depicted as
a prince seated on a swing and attended by
ladies. A swing festival was celebrated every
year during the rainy season and became a
popular feature of the Krishna cult.

the picture has still a sunny radiance, the nimble grace of only ten years previous
is wanting.

Between 1700 and 1750 a disturbed period follows in which this coarsening tendency
is maintained and variants of the earlier *Ragamalas* are executed with summary
brusqueness. Bundi state was involved at the time in turmoil and it is not until the
accession of Umed Singh (ruled 1744-71) that painting enters a new phase. Under this
ruler the royal visage is once again stamped on local painting, Umed Singh providing
the features not only of princely hunters but also of Baz Bahadur, formerly ruler of
Mandu but now a subject of romantic legend. The general agitation of the time seems
to have infected the painters and in pictures probably executed between 1750 and
1760, Vishnu on his bird vehicle, Garuda, (no. 15) storms down from angry skies as if
anarchic violence has been suddenly unloosed. It is perhaps from this time that a
vogue for "action pictures" of animals first becomes a Bundi speciality. Elephants are
shown fighting each other, pursuing lions, tigers and rhinoceroses, or, if chained
(no. 19), striving angrily to burst their bonds. In these pictures a new approach to
animals is apparent. There is, firstly, a passionate interest in speed, as if the spectacle
of creatures in violent motion conveyed some special thrill. There is, secondly, a
playful enjoyment of animal postures; a sentence in a Hindi poem rendered by
Pramod Chandra, "Summer like a drunken elephant comes storming in," suggests the
quiet glee with which fantastic caperings were, at times, regarded.

Between 1760 and 1780, two brothers, Rajas Ajit and Bishan Singh, account for yet
another phase of Bundi painting. Ajit, the elder, closely resembling Bishan, succeeded
his father in 1772 but died the same year. Bishan succeeded Ajit and ruled from 1772
to 1821. In later years he became obsessed by lion hunting but as a prince he seems to
have shared with his brother an almost adolescent fascination with scenes of amorous
dalliance. During the 17th century, Mughal painters had at times portrayed
semi-nude courtesans as if they were frantic with desire; and under the two brothers,
two different groups of pictures, based on Mughal models, obtained a wide vogue.
The first showed palace ladies in gorgeous green, white, and orange, clasped by avid
lovers or exasperated by their absence. The second, the so-called "white" paintings—
from the predominance of white in courtyard walls or moon-drenched terraces—
showed nude ladies standing on footstools after the bath, their white forms caressingly
defined by long strands of hair. Often a male figure—the blue-skinned Krishna or a
pale-skinned prince—spies on them from a nearby window, while in certain cases
(no. 16), the part of the unseen viewer is duplicated or replaced by a mirror, the lady
herself assuming the voyeur's role. In both groups, the male figure is once again a
royal person—Ajit or Bishan Singh—and thus, even in a phase of what Barrett has
called "pleasant lubricity," Bundi painters continued to flatter and exalt their local
patron.

12 PORTRAIT OF RAO BHAO SINGH OF BUNDI
(ruled 1659-1682) SEATED BEFORE HIS FATHER
RAO CHATTAR SAL (ruled 1631-1659).
c. 1670

9⁵/₁₆ x 7⁹/₁₆ (within borders)

Exhibited: Persian and Indian Miniatures,
Binney Collection, Portland Supplementary
Exhibition. Cat. no. 76 a.

The practice of portraying a living ruler with
his deceased father was fairly common in
Rajasthani painting. The shaded armpits,
shared by the two princes, were characteristic
of Mughal painting in the 16th and early
17th centuries. The title, *rao,* is the
Bundi equivalent of *raja.*

For portraits of Chattar Sal, Bhao Singh, and
their successors, see Hendley; Archer, *Bundi and
Kotah,* pls. 2, 3, 22 and 32; and Welch and
Beach, pl. 19.

गुजरीसागनी

13 **GUJARI RAGINI** From a *Ragamala* series.
c. 1670–80

$10\frac{3}{8}$ x 7

The inscriptions in the yellow band above the picture are, from left to right, the number in the complete *Ragamala* series given by a previous owner; the title in Persian characters (which suggests a Persian-reading owner) and, finally, the title of the miniature in *nagari* characters. Persian script was in official use not only at the Mughal imperial court but at many Rajput courts in Rajasthan, Central India, and the Punjab Hills.

The lady is awaiting the arrival of her lover. The *vina,* the stringed instrument held in her right hand, has not provided sufficient distraction to turn her thoughts away from him. The male peacock, feathers displayed in the courting ritual, does nothing to calm her longing.

Other leaves from this series have been reproduced in Archer (1956), pl. 7; Kanoria catalog, cover; Archer, *Bundi and Kotah,* pls. 6–9; Archer, *Indian Miniatures,* pl. 42; and in Lee, no. 27, p. 35. Other leaves are in the Victoria and Albert Museum, London, and the Kanoria collection, Calcutta.

14 Two illustrations from a *Rasika Priya* series.
c. 1670–80

a) RADHA APPROACHES KRISHNA'S BEDCHAMBER
$12\frac{1}{8}$ x $6\frac{3}{4}$

b) A CAMEL GRAZES BELOW THE BEDCHAMBER
OF RADHA AND KRISHNA
$11\frac{7}{8}$ x $7\frac{3}{8}$

Ponds with lotuses and ducks, ornamented turrets perched precariously on roofs, and lush vegetation with fanlike banana trees were common features of Bundi painting from the 17th to the 19th centuries.

Other leaves from this series have been reproduced in M. Chandra and Mehta (1962), pl. 5; Chandra, *Bundi,* pl. 5; Khajanchi catalog, no. 39a, fig. 42; Archer (1957b), pl. 28; Archer, *Bundi and Kotah,* pl. 14–15; and Archer, *Indian Miniatures,* pl. 43.

13 GUJARI
RAGINI
Bundi

15 GARUDA FLIES THROUGH THE NIGHT SKY
WITH LAKSHMI AND VISHNU Bundi

15 GARUDA FLIES THROUGH THE NIGHT SKY WITH
LAKSHMI AND VISHNU

c. 1760

7⅝ x 5¾

Garuda is the vehicle of the god Vishnu. He is
sometimes depicted with a human head, but
most often as a bird of the parrot family. In
this picture, he dwarfs his divine master.
Vishnu normally has four arms, each equipped
with a distinctive weapon (cf. no. 1 c). Here,
however, Garuda is carrying the mace and conch
shell of his master so that the god needs only
two arms. The large ribbed feathers of the
wings resemble the leaves of the banana trees
in no. 14.

For a similar, but larger, rendering of the
theme, see Archer, *Bundi and Kotah,* pl. 21.

16 THE WAITING MISTRESS SEES THE REFLECTION OF
HER MISSING LORD IN A MIRROR
c. 1760-70
11½ x 8
Ex Coll.: Sri Motichand Khajanchi
(reproduced in Khajanchi catalog, no. 42,
fig. 45).

The theme of Krishna spying upon Radha and
being reflected beside her in the mirror she is
holding occurs in the *Kavi Priya* of Keshava
Das, where the episode is called the *subha
darsana* (see M. Chandra and Mehta [1962],
pl. 4, for a Mewar example). This
literary text serves as a basis for pictures which
show a reigning prince spying upon his
mistress while she is bathing or preparing
herself for his arrival. In Bundi, during the
second half of the 18th century, a
distinctive "white palette" was used for this
kind of picture. The lotus pond and banana
trees continue to be featured.

Other pictures in a similar "white" style are
reproduced in Ashton (ed.) no. 462, pl. 93;
Archer, *Bundi and Kotah,* pl. 19; Chandra,
Bundi, pl. 10; Barrett and Gray, p. 148; and
Welch and Beach, no. 56.

17 KAKUBHA RAGINI From a *Ragamala* series.
c. 1770-80
13⅞ x 9½
The lady, Kakubha Ragini, walks through the
forest alone at night on her way to meet her
lover. Her solitary state is emphasized by the
pairs of birds which surround her (ducks in the
banana trees at the top; cranes in the pond at
the bottom; peacocks on either side of her).

18 RAWAT BHIM SINGH WITH COMPANIONS
AND A PRIEST Portrait group.
c. 1800

9½ x 12⅞

Exhibited: S. C. Welch collection, de Cordova
Museum, Lincoln, Massachusetts, summer,
1960, no. 16; Persian and Indian Miniatures,
Binney Collection, West Coast Tour, 1962-64.
Cat. no. 75 (Udaipur).

The inscription on the verso, in *nagari*
characters, reads: *gusahi ji sanjagar ji* (this is the
man at the extreme right) *rawat bhim singh ji*
(he is in the left center) *rawat suwahimeg ji*
(seated behind him on the left) *rawat urjan singh
ji* (lower right). The name of Bhim Singh
suggests the Rana of Mewar who ruled from
1778-1828. The man pictured, however, is not
a Rana, and the orange color in the turbans,
the blue-green of the background, and the
yellow of the grass fly-whisks is more typical of
Bundi than of Mewar.
The use of the hookah, or water-pipe, is not
confined to men or to the nobility. Nor is it
necessary to be seated to smoke it. In this
picture, however, the entirely male group is
indulging in something comparable to the
after-dinner cigars of European custom.

18 RAWAT BHIM SINGH WITH COMPANIONS AND A PRIEST Bundi

19 ATTENDANTS TRYING TO CONTROL A CRAZED
ELEPHANT Drawing.
c. 1800

12¼ x 17¾ (irregular)

Exhibited: Persian and Indian Miniatures,
Binney Collection, West Coast Tour, 1962-64.
Cat. no. 77.

In later Bundi painting, as well as that of
neighboring Kotah (see nos. 21-22) there
appears a host of coarse drawings of elephants
and hunting scenes. The massive spiral of the
elephant's body, struggling to escape his fetters,
underlines the common sense of the two small
figures at the right who seek escape. The spears
and tridents of the keepers will avail them little
if the elephant does break free.

19 ATTENDANTS TRYING TO CONTROL A CRAZED ELEPHANT Bundi

KOTAH

Kotah is a large state adjoining Bundi on the southeast, but until about 1700 it does not seem to have produced any painting. Early in the 18th century, however, a number of pictures based on Bundi models, begin to appear. The subjects include *Ragamalas, Baramasas* (The Twelve Months), the *Rasika Priya* (no. 20 a-b) and the adventures of Krishna. Here also Kotah rulers are introduced as models for heroes and, in certain pictures, Rajas Ram Singh I (1686-1708) and Arjun Singh (1720-24) can be seen sustaining these roles. While adopting Bundi types of composition and imagery, Kotah pictures of this type are marked by somewhat rickety structures and a preference for fantastic plumelike clouds. In the middle of the century, the Bundi interest in animals filtered into Kotah, but some important differences must be noted. Kotah, with its vast stretches of jungle filled with small twisted trees topped by bands of mauve rock, has a wilder, more romantic look; and in Kotah painting, it is the jungle, quite as much as the animals in it, which provides the main theme. The attitude of sportive ridicule sometimes found in Bundi painting is markedly absent, and—especially in the early period—Kotah artists simplified animal forms, less in the interests of rhythm, speed or humor than of romantic reverie and poetic wonder.

Under Raja Umed Singh (1771-1819) this attitude results in a style noticeably similar to that of the French painter, le douanier Rousseau. Trees with their trunks, leaves, and branches are shown with magnified detail; forms, including those of animals and cliffs, are given a naive dreamlike simplicity, and the whole jungle has at times the tapestried richness of a court in medieval Europe. In a picture dated 1770 Umed Singh himself is shown shooting tigers; in others his famous ancestors, such as Durjan Sal (1724-56), are portrayed as if in reverential homage.

Between Umed Singh (died 1819) and Ram Singh II (1828-66), there is a minor interlude under Kishor Singh during which no major change is apparent. With Ram Singh II, on the other hand, a new and lively personality enters the stage, and while the Kotah exploration of the jungle as a poetic and symbolic setting is maintained, it is the ruler himself with all his varied diversions who now becomes the chief focus. In many pictures still preserved in the palace at Kotah, among them examples dated 1831, 1833, 1845, and 1847, he appears engaged in such activities as drifting in a boat on the river Chambal, walking in a procession, feasting with his courtiers, riding an elephant on the top of a pavilion or bestriding a charger on his palace roof. Sorties in the jungle nonetheless remain a constant subject (nos. 21-22), but in place of the dreamlike distortions of the Umed Singh period, there is now a delight in accurate observation and delicate naturalism. In certain pictures a small herd of deer ranged around a young blue buck suggests that even in the sporting scenes the example and message of Krishna were not forgotten.

20 Two leaves from a *Rasika Priya* series.
c. 1720

a) KRISHNA KNOCKS ON THE PALACE OF RADHA

10⅜ x 6¼ (within all borders)

Again the Bundi-like turrets on the palace, looking as if they were ready to topple off at any time. The revetment of square panels under the battlements has already appeared in Bundi pictures (cf. nos. 14 a-b) but now has a distinctive green color. The black night sky, threaded with snakelike flashes of lightning, mirrors the anxiety of the lovers (cf. no. 68). Clogs such as those worn by Krishna are very necessary during the Indian rainy season.

b) TWO MAIDS PREPARE A LADY FOR THE
   ARRIVAL OF HER LOVER

10⅞ x 5⅞ (within all borders)

Here, a different lady awaits a different lord. It is still night, but the sky is light, full of stars and with a full moon.

21 RAM SINGH II OF KOTAH (ruled 1828-1866)
SHOOTING TIGERS
Drawing with touches of color.
c. 1820

16½ x 12

Ram Singh II was a tremendous hunter of tigers and other game. Here shown as a prince before his succession in 1828, he is seated in a shooting platform which has been built into a tree. Beaters have driven the prey through the jungle and the prince has already begun the slaughter.

22 RAM SINGH II OF KOTAH SHOOTING TIGERS
FROM A PAVILION
Drawing with washes of color.
c. 1820

9¼ x 12⅜

Here the royal hunter is shown in a permanent shooting pavilion rather than in a simple hide-out. The scene is more complete than in no. 21, the beaters being shown as they drive the beasts before them. The lower inscription reads: *kota ri sri ram singh ji*.

21 RAM SINGH II
OF KOTAH
SHOOTING TIGERS
Kotah

22 RAM SINGH II OF KOTAH SHOOTING TIGERS FROM A PAVILLION   Kotah

Kishangarh, a small state sixty miles northwest of Bundi, was founded c. 1609 by Kishan Singh as an offshoot from Jodhpur. Until the late 17th century there is little evidence of painting, but from the early 18th century to the third quarter of the 19th, quantities of pictures were produced. Although their subjects included animals, hunting scenes, portraits of neighboring rulers as well as illustrations of the *Bhagavata Purana,* by far their chief theme was courtly love. This was expressed in studies of palace ladies (nos. 25, 26, 28), portraits of Kishangarh rulers (no. 27) and in renderings of Radha and Krishna (no. 24). Despite some early influence from Bikaner, Kishangarh painting derived in general from the 18th century Mughal styles of Delhi and Oudh and thus stood in sharp contrast to Rajput painting in Mewar, Bundi and Malwa. As in the Punjab Hills, the fussy banalities of later Mughal painting were normally avoided and delicate refinements of technique were linked to a sense of lyrical poetry and dignified charm.

Amongst eight hundred pictures which were seen by Eric Dickinson in 1943 in the Maharaja of Kishangarh's collection, a tiny group of unusually large miniatures, measuring in some cases as much as eighteen inches by fifteen, require special comment. Two are ascribed in marginal notes to a particular painter, Nihal Chand. Another, of a music party featuring Raja Sardar Singh (1757-66) with courtiers and dancing girls, is inscribed with the name of a second artist, Amar Chand; and a fourth expressly illustrates a verse by a devotional poet, Nagari Das. This last name conceals the identity of a Kishangarh poet-prince, Savant Singh (born 1699, died 1764).

Savant Singh's influence on Kishangarh painting is generally regarded as decisive. Like certain other rulers in Rajasthan and Central India, he was an accomplished poet and a religious devotee. The writing of poetry, though rare, was not unknown among Rajput rulers. It was also not unusual for Rajput princes to abandon administration in favor of the religious life. Savant Singh was exceptional because he combined both roles. His poems, written under the name of Nagari Das, celebrated Krishna's great romance and expressed his own sense of personal identification with Krishna. In about 1740 he had fallen in love with a bewitching singer and poetess, Bani Thani, and from the mid-forties onwards had lived with her outside the state of Kishangarh in the groves of Brindaban, the actual scene of Krishna's youth. In 1748 his father, Raj Singh, died, and, perhaps influenced by Savant Singh's indifference to administration, his younger brother, Bahadur Singh (1748-81) seized the state, leaving Savant Singh to dwell in Brindaban or go on pilgrimages. In 1756 Savant Singh regained a part of Kishangarh but almost immediately abdicated in favor of his son,

Sardar Singh, and withdrew once more to Brindaban where he died in 1764. His genius as a poet of Krishna, his religious devotion, and his romance with Bani Thani— comparable to that of the great lovers of Central India, Baz Bahadur and Rupmati— had obviously made a great impact on Kishangarh life, and many pictures inspired by his verses were produced. It seems unlikely, however, that any of the large miniatures noted above were painted in Kishangarh under his personal patronage, since, apart from only a brief return in 1756, he was absent from the state from 1748 to 1764. Moreover, the fact that his son, Sardar Singh, rather than he himself, is shown presiding at a music party in the palace, as well as the absence of any authenticated contemporary portraits of Savant Singh, suggest that it was under Sardar Singh, the son, rather than the father, that these masterpieces began to be produced. Although Sardar Singh's *Music Party* is by the artist Amar Chand (dateable to the years 1760 to 1765 on account of Sardar Singh's apparent age), its style is broadly similar to that of Nihal Chand, the second artist noted. Others of these large miniatures could well have been done early in the reign of Sardar Singh's adopted son and successor, Birad Singh (1766-88), who also seems to have been influenced by Savant Singh's extraordinary career.

This tiny group of large miniatures, perhaps painted in the years 1757 to 1770, constitute Kishangarh painting at its greatest height. With the exception of Sardar Singh's *Music Party*, all celebrate romantic encounters between Radha and Krishna and all show them in scenes of courtly splendor. In most cases, the two protagonists appear as tiny figures in vast surroundings (see no. 24)—a great lake or a receding landscape with thick woods conveying a sense of timeless infinitude or a tranced removal from ordinary life. In one picture the opposite convention is employed, and Radha, shown head and schoulders, is so magnified as almost to mesmerize the beholder by her grandeur. Throughout the entire group runs a hauntingly mannered type of facial idiom. This is at times employed for Radha and Krishna alone; in other cases it includes their feminine companions, and in the *Music Party* it is seen in both the dancing girls and their boy attendants. This special kind of face is characterized by a receding forehead, sharp out-thrusting nose and chin, long curving eye and domed eyebrows. As in Bundi, this distinctive idiom may well have been inspired by the actual features of members of the local royal family, though in the paintings under discussion it far transcends any immediate likeness to a particular prince.

During the period 1770 to 1860, large miniatures seem to have gone out of fashion though an entry in the Kishangarh State archives dated 1773, ordering the painter

Nihal Chand to be supplied with gold-leaf, shows that he was still at work and possibly still a prime influence. Aspects of the great masterpieces, however, continued to influence painting (see nos. 24 and 25), and the early cult of courtly love obtained renewed expression in smaller studies of palace ladies, standing or seated on terraces and holding in their hands wine cups and betel leaves (nos. 26 and 28). Their faces still resemble the stylized beauties of the earlier period though in some cases the formula is carried to overviolent extremes (no. 29). A painting of Bahadur Singh (1748-81), the younger brother of Savant Singh and rival ruler of Kishangarh, shows him, perhaps in 1780, with white hair, worshipping at a shrine to Kalyan Rai (i.e. Krishna) and surrounded by courtiers and palace ladies whose faces continue to show this same sophisticated image. Yet another picture, a handsome study of Kishan Singh (no. 27) founder of the Kishangarh line, has not only the ivory flesh tones common to Bikaner painting of the late 18th century, but also a purple and greenish yellow dress with gold braidings—details which convincingly ally him to the courtly ladies of nos. 26 and 28 whose dresses share the same colors.

In 1820 a series of pictures was painted for Raja Kalyan Singh (1797-1838) illustrating the *Gita Govinda*. In this series the supremacy of the Kishangarh face is seemingly under challenge, though the treatment of the countryside with its springing bamboos—strikingly similar to Kotah paintings of the same period—goes far to authenticate its dated colophon. Another picture of about 1840 shows Mokham Singh (1838-41) standing with his courtiers by a lake, similar in its empty vastness to those in the great masterpieces. In a second picture, Prithvi Singh (1841-80) rides with his son in an arid landscape which is equally deserted. This picture, dateable to about 1860, comes at a time when, despite a continued use of earlier idioms, Kishangarh painting had declined in sensitivity and refinement. The *mystique* of the style, however, has continued to enchant recent students of Rajput painting, and has even encouraged a living Jaipur artist, Vijayavargiya, to produce a number of attractive pastiches. These recent interpretations, sometimes mistaken for earlier originals, suggest how beguilingly modern in spirit was Kishangarh painting at the height of its achievement.

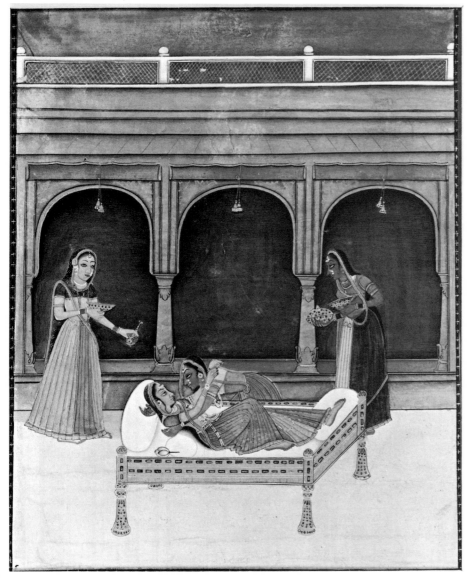

23 A SICK LADY, PERHAPS RADHA, LIES ON A BED, SUPPORTED BY A MAID

c. 1750

$8\frac{3}{4}$ x $6\frac{5}{8}$

The special type of face connected with Kishangarh is already apparent in the ladies, though not yet completely stylized to the almost grotesque extent encountered later (see no. 29). The flat architectural plane gives no hint of perspective. Since many of Krishna's female conquests "swoon with love" or "become sick with love" of him, the principal figure here may well be Radha.

24 RADHA AND KRISHNA ON A GARDEN TERRACE
BY A LAKE
c. 1760
$10^3/_8$ x $7^3/_{16}$ (within borders)

Radha and Krishna, sharing the same halo,
pluck lotus flowers and throw them into a
lake. The mood is utterly calm; their solitude
is complete. The full development of the
Kishangarh face is already in evidence, in
spite of the tiny size of the figures in this early
picture. There is none of the hardening of the
features noticeable later in no. 29. The problems
of perspective have been realized and worked
with. The backward-leaning balustrades of the
rug-covered terrace and the central square
enclosure where the bed has been set up seem
incomplete. The identical beds of flowers
receding toward the avenue of fountains in the
background is a convention found in
contemporary miniatures from the provincial
Mughal capital of Murshidabad and the
Central Indian state of Datia (see Welch and
Beach, nos. 38 and 42).

25 A LADY SEATED
ON A RAISED COUCH
IS ATTENDED BY
HER TWO MAIDS
Kishangarh
Color plate page 8

25 A LADY SEATED ON A RAISED COUCH IS
ATTENDED BY HER TWO MAIDS
In the distance, the view of a walled town with
an elaborate waterfront.
c. 1770
$13\frac{1}{2}$ x $8\frac{3}{8}$
In this miniature the pattern of horizontal bands
of landscape noted before (no. 24) has become
even more complex. There are now three
bodies of water, two of them lotus ponds and
the third a segment of a wide river. There are
also three bands of landscape and three bands
of buildings. The center of interest is the
diagonal group formed by the lady and her
two maids and attendant peacocks; this group
is reflected by the boat in the distant river.
The asymmetry of the picture, its major groups
slightly to the right of the vertical axis (the
ladies, the boat, the distant hilltop castle) is
already heralded by the open space in the front
balustrade of the terrace on which the lady
is sitting. The "Y-shaped" water entrances to
the boathouses in the center attempt to restore
a central orientation. The lady shows the
Kishangarh eye, as do both of her attendant
maids.

26 A LADY SEATED ON A RUG, LEANING
AGAINST A BOLSTER
c. 1770–80
$8^3/_{16}$ x $5^3/_4$
Again the special type of face associated with
Kishangarh painting. The lady holds a tiny
wine cup in her left hand and a betel leaf in her
left. Storm clouds are shown as a line of
almost identical spirals with gilded edges.

27 RAJA KISHAN SINGH OF KISHANGARH
(ruled c. 1609–1615) SALUTING
c. 1770–80
$13^3/_4$ x $6^1/_8$ (mat opening)
The damaged condition of this portrait in no
way detracts from its quality. Kishan Singh
was a prince from a cadet line of the house of
the rulers of Jodhpur. In personal favor with
the Mughal Emperor Jahangir (ruled 1605–
1625), he was allowed to set up the separate
state of Kishangarh about 1609, to which he
gave his own name. The green background
behind the royal figure suggests that this may
be an 18th century copy of an original of the
time of Jahangir. He is shown saluting and
holding a sword, a pose that suggests an act of
obeisance, presumably towards his Mughal
overlord. This also underlines the probability
of the picture being a copy of an earlier work.
The bright red paint which shows through
where the top layer has flaked is a common
undercoat in Indian miniatures.

28 STANDING LADY WITH
A CUP AND BOWL
IN HER HANDS
Kishangarh

29 A LADY, PERHAPS RADHA,
IN PROFILE,
GAZING FROM A WINDOW
Kishangarh

27 RAJA KISHAN SINGH
OF KISHANGARH SALUTING
Kishangarh

28 STANDING LADY WITH A CUP AND BOWL
IN HER HANDS
c. 1780
$10\frac{1}{2}$ x $6\frac{5}{8}$

This beauty seems to be an attendant at court.
Attendants like her may be found in the great
Kishangarh masterpieces still preserved in the
royal collection of that state. The gold in the
lightly washed background, streaked to suggest
sun on hazy clouds, appears also in later
Mughal pictures (cf. Welch [1963], no. 78.)

29 A LADY (perhaps Radha) IN PROFILE, GAZING
FROM A WINDOW
c. 1790
$7\frac{1}{2}$ x $5\frac{1}{8}$

The formalization of the "Kishangarh face"
is here complete. What started as a magnificent
aberration has now become a stereotyped
convention with no aura of divine mystery.
The lady stares from her window. Fingering
the veil whose fringed decoration is repeated
on her right shoulder, she seems more like a
courtesan than the beloved of the cowherd god.

OTHER RAJASTHANI STYLES

Besides the four states discussed above, other parts of Rajasthan also developed distinctive styles of Rajput painting. In Marwar, a great tract northwest of Mewar, Jodhpur, the capital, specialized in scenes of courtly life. There, the Rajput interest in swaggering rhythm and haughty stances found early expression, but it was in the second half of the 18th century, when huge and toppling turbans were the fashion, that the special brand of Jodhpur sophistication reached its apogee (nos. 32, 33). In Bikaner, immediately to the north, coarse derivatives of imperial Mughal painting (no. 30) preceded an incursion of Mughal-trained artists in the second half of the 17th century, their styles (no. 31) owing much to the separate tradition of painting in the Deccan. Further east at Jaipur, proximity to the imperial Mughal capitals of Delhi and Agra prevented the rise of any strongly independent styles in the 17th and early 18th centuries. In 1728, however, the construction of a new city at Jaipur on European lines by Raja Jai Singh II (1700-44) led to an influx of Western engravings. Their presence resulted in a conscious adaptation of Western-style perspective to local needs (no. 38) and the production of townscapes based on Western models.

In addition to the state capitals, local baronies or *thikanas* also at times developed local styles of painting. In the state of Marwar, distinctive sub-styles can be found in the baronies of Pali, Nagaur, Ghanerao and others. In the state of Ajmer, the *thikana* of Sawar gave an oddly noble distinction to its sparse renderings of Mughal-type ladies (no. 34); and in the state of Jaipur, Malpura, a barony on the southwest, evolved a hesitantly hybrid style (nos. 35, 36) in which influences from Jodhpur, Bundi, and Central India can all be detected.

30 NATA RAGINI
Bikaner

44

30 NATA RAGINI From a *Ragamala* series.
Bikaner
c. 1640–50
10⅛ x 7⅝

It seems surprising to see fighting men
representing a "female musical mode," the
ragini. One must remember, however, that it is
not the scene depicted, but rather the mood,
which suggests the difference between *ragas* and
raginis. Bikaner submitted early to the Mughals
and there is strong Mughal influence in its
pictures. It is a desert state, and this painting
shows a bare hillock with the sparse trees and
spongy rocks found in Mughal and Persian
landscapes. No longer present is the luxurious
vegetation of the jungle states of Bundi
and Kotah.

31 A LADY FLEES FROM A PRINCE ON A TERRACE
Bikaner
c. 1690
8¹⁵/₁₆ x 5⅛

In this Bikaner picture, which is somewhat later
than the preceding one, a higher degree of
sophistication is obvious, and the young noble
looks very like those of the same period at
Delhi, the Mughal court.

32 A NOBLEMAN, RECLINING ON A TERRACE,
ATTENDED BY HIS LADIES
Jodhpur
c. 1790
9⅞ x 13 (within borders)
Exhibited: Persian and Indian Miniatures,
Binney Collection, Portland Supplementary

Exhibition. Cat. no. 80 a.

Jodhpur artists borrowed from many schools
before developing their own equestrian
portrait style (see no. 33). Here a noble lies at
ease. He is wearing a long turban similar to the
upright one favored by Raja Ram Singh of
Jodhpur during his short reign in 1750. He is

surrounded by opulence: attendant maids, lush
vegetation, plentiful birds and by the cupolas
of Mughal and Rajput palaces. The goose
interrogating a pair of peacocks in the
foreground appears to parallel the maid who is
about to give the prince a fragrant garland of
white flowers.

32 A NOBLEMAN, RECLINING ON A TERRACE, ATTENDED BY HIS LADIES   Jodhpur

34 A GIRL STANDING BENEATH A WILL
HOLDING A "TAMBURA"
Sawar (Ajmer)

33 PORTRAIT OF RAJA RAM SINGH
OF JODHPUR ON HORSEBACK
Jodhpur

33 PORTRAIT OF RAJA RAM SINGH OF JODHPUR
ON HORSEBACK
Jodhpur
c. 1840
10¾ x 8⅞
Inscribed in *nagari* characters: *sabi maharaja sri ram singh ji ki* "Portrait of Maharaja

Sri Ram Singh."
Indian portraits often depict earlier members of a reigning royal house. Raja Ram Singh of Jodhpur reigned for only one year (1750). He is posthumously portrayed here in the equestrian pose typical of late Jodhpur portraits. He wears the towering turban fashionable during his reign.

35 UDHO TAKES LEAVE OF KRISHNA WHO THEN ASSEMBLES THE YADAVAS   Malpura (Jaipur)

34 A GIRL STANDING BENEATH A WILLOW
HOLDING A "TAMBURA"
Sawar (Ajmer)
c. 1720
13 x 8⁹/₁₆
Inscribed in *nagari* characters: *mahari tamburo bajao chhai* "Mahari is playing the *tambura*."
Ajmer, one of the Rajasthani states nearest to the Mughal capital of Delhi, was early conquered by Muslim invaders. Sawar, one of its *thikanas* (fiefs), shares with its parent state a typical "not completely painted" look, well exemplified by this miniature. The unpainted background is not the result of failure to finish the picture but rather of concentration on the major decorative elements to the exclusion of non-essentials.

35 UDHO TAKES LEAVE OF KRISHNA WHO THEN
ASSEMBLES THE YADAVAS   From a *Bhagavata Purana* series.
Malpura (Jaipur)
c. 1775
10 x 15⁹/₁₆
Malpura is a *thikana* of the state of Jaipur in Eastern Rajasthan to which miniature paintings have only recently been assigned. Here, as in certain early Italian paintings, different episodes are presented as though occurring simultaneously. The bands of vegetation in the central axis of the picture are purely decorative. This leaf illustrates a late episode in the *Bhagavata Purana*. Udho, the friend and confidant of Krishna, is sent away before the final battle in which Krishna's kinsmen, the Yadavas, will perish. (See no. 77 for a scene from this battle.)

47

36 MALKAUS RAGA From a *Ragamala* series.
Malpura (Jaipur), by the artist Ram Kishen.
1786

$12\frac{3}{4}$ x $8\frac{5}{8}$

This picture comes from a series of which one
leaf, formerly in the collection of Eric
Schroeder, Cambridge, Massachusetts, and now
in the Fogg Art Museum, Harvard University,
is inscribed with the date and artist's name as
given above.

Another leaf from this series is in the Victoria
and Albert Museum, London.

37 SHIVA AND PARVATI RIDING
ON A MANY-DEWLAPPED NANDI
Jaipur

37 SHIVA AND PARVATI RIDING ON A
MANY-DEWLAPPED NANDI
Jaipur
c. 1770
8⅜ x 5⁵⁄₁₆

Here Shiva and his consort Parvati ride
together on his vehicle, Nandi the bull. Shiva is
easily recognizable: his color white in strong
contrast to the blue of Vishnu; third eye in the
middle of his forehead; the snakes he wears as
necklace and the river Ganges which springs
from his hair marked by the wavy white line
on the left of the picture.

38 SHIVA AND PARVATI WITH THEIR SON GANESHA
ON A TERRACE ABOVE A CITY
Jaipur
c. 1790
12⅜ x 8⅝

The divine couple are resting on a tree-shaded
terrace. Shiva, with a necklace and armlet of
snakes, supports himself with his arm. His
drooping head shows other snakes in his hair,
and the river Ganges falling from the topknot
(cf. no. 37 where the river is more pronounced).
He ignores the cup offered by Parvati and
similarly pays no attention to his son, the
elephant-headed Ganesha, behind him.
Ganesha, the god of learning, is often depicted
with one broken tusk (broken from having
used it as a pen, for he is also the patron of
scribes). On both sides of the terrace stand
groups of Shaivite priests, their piled hair
resembling their Lord's.

38 SHIVA AND PARVATI
WITH THEIR SON GANESHA
ON A TERRACE ABOVE A CITY
Jaipur

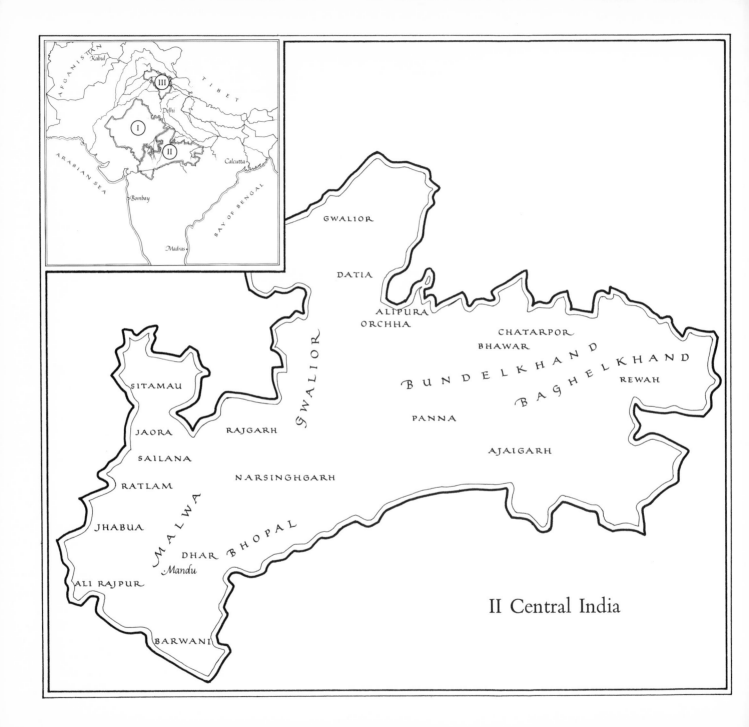

Kabul
AFGANISTAN
TIBET
III
Delhi
I
ARABIAN SEA
II
Calcutta
BAY OF BENGAL
Bombay
Madras

GWALIOR

DATIA

ALIPURA
ORCHHA

CHATARPOR
BHAWAR

B U N D E L K H A N D

B A G H E L K H A N D

REWAH

PANNA

AJAIGARH

SITAMAU

GWALIOR

JAORA

RAJGARH

SAILANA

RATLAM

NARSINGHGARH

MALWA

JHABUA

DHAR BHOPAL

Mandu

ALI RAJPUR

BARWANI

II Central India

II Central India

Central India, 540 miles long and 270 miles wide, was approximately the same length as Rajasthan but was almost 200 miles narrower. Lying immediately to the southeast of Rajasthan, its shape resembled a broadly based triangle. On the east it followed in general the course of the river Jamuna. On the west it adjoined Mewar, while to the south it was bounded by the river Narbada, traditional frontier between north and south India. Within this broad triangle, it included four distinct tracts.

Gwalior, at the apex, had been a Rajput stronghold until, in 1523, its ruler, Man Singh Tonwar, was defeated by the Mughal emperor Babur. It was then annexed by the Mughals and had remained Mughal until the 18th century when the Marathas swarmed over central India. These plundering adventurers from the south founded a number of new states and attached to them a series of isolated enclaves of territory. Two thirds of Maratha Gwalior were in the northern part of Central India, its remaining third was scattered over the western part of Malwa.

The second tract of Central India was in the south and center but, apart from the Muslim state of Bhopal, was inhabited by forest tribes. It was non-Rajput in culture and is not, therefore, of present concern.

The third tract, Bundelkhand (with Baghelkhand)—roughly 100 miles wide and 300 miles long—ran southeast from Gwalior parallel to the Jamuna. In the 16th century, a Rajput ruler of Orchha, Bir Singh Deo, had controlled almost all this great area, but later it had been split up into eight separate Rajput states—Datia, Alipura, Orchha, Panna, Chhatarpur, Bijawar, Ajaigarh and Rewah. Rewah in Baghelkhand was at the southernmost extremity and was important because it was only sixty miles from Jaunpur, a Muslim center which may have influenced early Central Indian painting.

The fourth part of Central India was Malwa itself—a large region, 300 miles long and 130 miles wide, adjoining Mewar on the southeast. At its northern end Kotah jutted deeply into it, virtually severing it from Gwalior. Like Bundelkhand, Malwa had, at one time, been a single great unit governed not by Rajputs, but by Muslims. Rajputs, however, had formed in many areas a major part of the population. Certain Muslim rulers had been strongly pro-Rajput, and although from the 16th to 18th centuries, Mandu, its capital, was Muslim-controlled, strong Rajput influences were present in its culture. Subsequently, under the later Mughals, Rajput areas in Malwa became the separate Rajput states of Rajgarh, Narsinghgarh, Ratlam, Sitamau, Sailana, Jhabua, Barwani, and Ali Rajpur. These were intermixed with Muslim and Maratha states and enclaves and, as in other parts of Central India, were in general not territorial unities, as in Rajasthan, but collections of scattered villages, as jumbled and disparate as the pieces of a jigsaw puzzle.

During the 15th and 16th centuries painting at Mandu, the capital of Malwa, passed through three phases. The first (1400-75) was a variant of the Jain style of Western India and was devoted to Jain scriptures of special interest to the Jain trading community. The second (1490-1531) developed under its Muslim Sultans, the Khiljis, and was an Indian offshoot of the Turkman style of Shiraz in Persia, blended at times with influence from Bukhara. The third flourished under the Pathans (1535-61), and besides combining elements of these two previous styles, may also have reflected influences from eastern India (Jaunpur). Under the Pathan emperor, Sher Shah (died 1545)—rival first to the Lodis and then to the Mughals—Malwa was incorporated in the Pathan empire, coming first under a Pathan governor and a little later under independent Pathan rule. For painting of this time, a key patron was probably Baz Bahadur (ruled 1554-61), to whose poetic stimulus as a prince the *Laur Chanda* and *Chaurapanchasika* (Mewar q.v.) can plausibly be ascribed. The *Laur Chanda,* "Romance of Lorik and the lady Chandaini," was a poem extolling two lovers of Eastern and Central India. The *Chaurapanchasika,* "Fifty Stanzas of Secret Love," celebrated a poet's intrigue with a king's daughter. These secular nondevotional texts were highly romantic and hence afford a close parallel to Baz Bahadur's celebrated romance with the Hindu courtesan and poetess, Rupmati. Their illustrations are notable for chic ferocity, sophisticated elegance, and commanding rhythm, as well as for details such as square-shaped heads, great enlarged eyes, flat backgrounds in red, green and black, and schematic trees. The closest precursors of this style are a Jain *Kalpa Sutra* painted at Jaunpur in 1465 and a *Vanaparva* manuscript illustrated in 1516 at a place described as Kachchhauva. The exact whereabouts of Kachchhauva are still debatable, but if it is identified as Kachhawa, it would lie less than one hundred miles southeast of Jaunpur. Jaunpur lay within the Pathan empire of Sher Shah at whose instance the Pathans had occupied Malwa. Painters either from Jaunpur itself, or aware of Jaunpur experiments, might therefore have inoculated the second phase of painting in Mandu with Jaunpur-type ingredients, thus producing the marvelous sets so closely geared to Baz Bahadur's private life. It is of interest that N. C. Mehta obtained the *Chaurapanchasika* in Partabgarh, a town in Eastern India which is only forty miles west of Jaunpur.

Following the sack of Mandu by Mughal armies in 1561 and Baz Bahadur's replacement by a Mughal Governor, painting in Malwa seems to have gone underground. Seventy years later, however, it reappears in Rajgarh, a Rajput state in Malwa, one hundred and fifty miles northeast of Mandu. At this time, Rajgarh was ruled by Chattar Singh (1621-38), a raja who had already asserted some degree of freedom from the Mughals. His young successor, Mohan Singh (1638-97) was dominated first by a Regent, Ajab Singh, and later by Raja Parasram (died 1697). In 1675 the latter enforced a division of the state's villages between himself and Mohan Singh and in 1681 proclaimed a separate state with the newly built town of Narsinghgarh as capital. Narsingh (man-lion incarnation of Vishnu) was Parasram's favorite deity and it is possible that the phrase *narsing shahar,* "City of Narsingh," on a dated *Ragamala* of 1680, may either refer to the new state and capital planned for creation a year later or be a pseudonym for Rajgarh where Raja Parasram had hitherto lived and worshipped. Other incarnations of Vishnu, prominent in the religious life of Rajgarh and Narsinghgarh, were Rama and Krishna.

The first Rajput paintings to revive the Mandu style in Rajgarh include a *Rasika Priya* dated 1634 (no. 40), a *Ramayana* of about 1630 (no. 39 a-b), and two parallel but distinct *Bhagavata Puranas* (nos. 41, 42), both of perhaps the year 1640. In this first phase the flaunting distortions of the early style have been modified, but idioms such as a wavy white band on the skyline, trees reduced to schematic ovals, flat backgrounds of color, and bleakly simple arrangements of figures all suggest, in summary and primitive form, the Mandu masterpieces. These traits of style are extended at Rajgarh in the next fifty years, but unlike Mewar where Rajput painting had developed from the same Mandu source, a bolder, more symbolic and less literal approach to form and content was frankly adopted. Negations of natural scenery such as broad expanses of rich chocolate-brown and deep slate-blue were freely employed. Distortions such as a slashing curve for a pond (no. 44) or two great wheels for revolving dancers (no. 48) gave the pictures a bold air of geometric poetry. Toppling trees (no. 42) were built up out of individual leaves and exuded a sluggish air of suave luxuriance. Above all, flat expanses of scarlet, used in much previous painting as a means for heightening tension, were manipulated with gay abandon. Human figures, whether isolated or in groups, were shown against red backgrounds like theatre back-cloths, private auras, or glowing emanations, as if the very act of being human and alive implied the generation of passionate feeling. Indeed, so vital an attribute was this scarlet background that any show of quasi-natural appearance was recklessly abandoned. In no. 44, the red background to the four figures is arbitrarily slotted into the brown hillside, and in no. 45 a, *Asavari Ragini,* engaged in a fierce tug-of-war with snakes, has the same red background incongruously lapped by fringing rocks.

Until about the year 1730, this vehement and dramatic style seems to have dominated painting in Rajgarh and Narsinghgarh, relying throughout on the same flat conventions, the same palette, and the same compartmental type of pictorial construction. Early in the 18th century, however, Sawai Jai Singh of Jaipur attacked Rajgarh, levying from Raja Amar Singh (1697-1740) a crippling tribute, and, a little later in the century, the Marathas imposed their rule on Central India. There is no evidence that Rajput painting in Rajgarh survived this onslaught, though elsewhere in Central India, *Ragamala* pictures of a well-known type but uncertain provenance (nos. 51 and 52) were probably produced about the middle of the century. In Datia, further to the northeast in Bundelkhand, a minor school of painting (no. 50) developed in the 18th century, the features of the Datia rulers providing, as in Bundi, models for ideal lovers. It seems unlikely that Datia pictures were produced in great quantities for when, in recent years, the collection of the Datia Rajas was dispersed, many of the pictures proved to be in the Malwa style of Rajgarh and were explained to Khandalavala as having come "from a nearby area about a hundred years ago." It is significant that a *Ragamala,* now in the Birla collection, Calcutta, but until recently in the Raja of Narsinghgarh's family collection, is in identically the same Rajgarh-Narsinghgarh style.

It is rather to a region remote from Malwa that we must look for a final flowering of this Central Indian style. Nepal, on the eastern frontier of India, had its own Rajput community which over the centuries had kept in close touch with Rajputs elsewhere. Nepali Rajputs intermarried with the Rajputs of Rajasthan, Central India, and Bihar. There were also Nepali temples at famous places of pilgrimage such as Banaras. On the collapse of painting in Rajgarh in the mid-18th century, one or more painters skilled in the Rajgarh style of Malwa painting may therefore have made the long journey to Nepal and there produced for Nepali Rajput patrons a number of pictures, among them a *Bhagavata Purana* (no. 49). This great series, obtained from a family at Khatmandu, has a larger format than was usual in Central India, and is slightly more complex in construction. It has otherwise all the marks of Central Indian painting—a fondness for slightly jagged forms and angular geometric constructions, a palette of glowing reds and deep slate-blues, and the same compulsive welding together of the picture's constituents. Only, in fact, in details such as the temple architecture with its tall towers and long finials, Krishna's profile and Nepali crown, and finally the treatment of the great stars, shining like lamps against a slate-blue sky, does Nepal reveal its haunting presence.

39 Two leaves from a *Ramayana* series.
Rajgarh (Malwa)
c. 1630

a) THE FOREST DEMONS SUBMIT TO RAMA
AND LAKSHMANA

7 x 9

Exhibited: Persian and Indian Miniatures,
Binney Collection, West Coast Tour,
1962-64. Cat. no. 54.

In the *Ramayana,* the hero is Rama. Like
Krishna, he is an avatar or incarnation of the
god Vishnu and is, therefore, pictured blue.
His half-brother is Lakshmana, who, like
Krishna's half-brother Balarama, is usually
portrayed like his divine brother, but painted
white. The brothers enlist the aid of monkey
and bear armies to attack the fortress of the
demon king Ravana at Lanka (Ceylon).
Ravana has carried off Sita, the wife of Rama.
Early in the story, Rama and his brother live in
a wood where they help their neighbors, the
ascetics, by defeating a series of forest demons
whom they pardon rather than kill.

b) SITA CALLS UPON FIRE TO WITNESS TO
HER CHASTITY

$7\frac{1}{8}$ x $9\frac{1}{8}$

After her abduction by Ravana, and her
recapture by Rama, Sita needs to prove her
chastity in the face of her long enforced
captivity. Here she is surrounded by flames,
while Rama, Lakshmana, and Hanuman, leader
of the monkey armies, watch her ordeal.

Leaves from this *Ramayana* series have been
reproduced in the Kanoria catalog, pl. VII;
Archer (1958), pl. 6; Archer, *Indian Miniatures,*
pl. 34; Lee and Archer (1963), no. 13; Khajanchi
catalog, no. 49, fig. 47; and Lee, no. 6, p. 18.
The largest part of the series is in Bharat Kala
Bhavan, Banaras. Other leaves are in the
Archer, Kanoria, and Khajanchi collections.

39b SITA CALLS UPON FIRE
TO WITNESS TO HER CHASTITY
Rajgarh (Malwa)

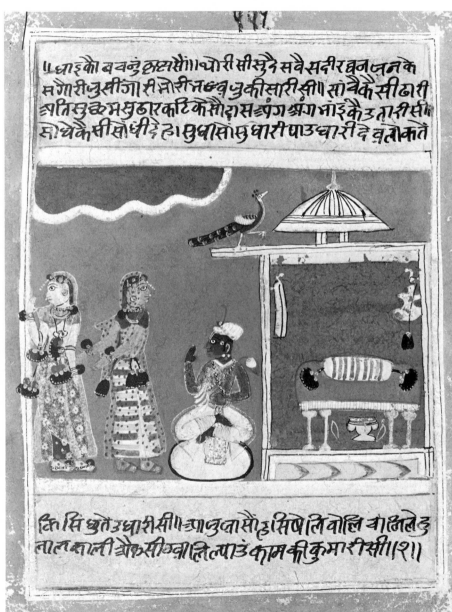

॥धाइकौ बचनु अट्यासैौ॥जोरी सीसुदै सवै सदीर वन जन के
सगौरी नुसीजा सी नोरी जब्ब चुकीसारी सी॥ सौ नैकै सीढारी
व्रतिसुख समुठारकटि कै सौरासप्रगा श्रृगा भाई कै उ तारी सी
सौ नैकै सीधी दे हा मुखासी सुधारी पाउचारी दे व्रतोकते

कि सि छुते उधारी सी॥ पाउचा सौ हृ सि बेलि नोलि बाक्षिल दु
नालकाली ऑक्सी ग्वालि ल्याउ काम की कुमारी सी॥।१३॥

40 THE LOVER SEES THE APPROACH OF HIS MISTRESS
From a *Rasika Priya* series.
Rajgarh (Malwa)
Dated 1634
5 1/4 x 4 1/2
Exhibited: Persian and Indian Miniatures,
Binney Collection, West Coast Tour, 1962-64.
Cat. no. 53.

The lady appears with some trepidation on the
left, but is admonished by her maid. The
waiting lover sits outside the empty bedchamber.
On the roof above is a peacock. The black
pompons of female adornment worn on
bracelets (here duplicated by the tassels of the
bolster on the bed) are common in this and
other contemporary series, being a legacy of
earlier miniatures. They have figured in Mewar
pictures (nos. 1, 2, 4, and 5), but seldom occur
after the end of the 17th century.

Leaves from this series have been reproduced in
Khandalavala, *Marg* (1950), fig. 15; Zimmer,
I, pl. C4; Lee, 5 d, p. 17 and the McNear
catalog, no. 8.
The bulk of the series is in the National
Museum, New Delhi. Other leaves are in art
museums in Boston, Cleveland, Philadelphia,
and Seattle, in London at the Victoria and
Albert Museum and in the Bickford and
Wyman collections.
Note: The series is assigned to Rajgarh,
parent state of Narsinghgarh in Malwa,
because of various distinctive idioms and
details which recur in an inscribed *Ragamala*
series, dated 1680, specifically noted as having
been prepared at Narsinghgarh.

41 Two leaves from a *Bhagavata Purana* series.
Rajgarh (Malwa)
c. 1640
6¾ x 7½
Ex Coll.: Maharaja of Datia (Bundelkhand), Central India.

a) KRISHNA, WITH ONE OF HIS EIGHT QUEENS, SEATED WITH THEIR DAUGHTER AND TEN SONS

Krishna, divinely prolific, has eight queens from each of whom he has one daughter and ten sons. The artist needed a double register in the picture to portray all the children of a single queen.

b) KRISHNA AND AKRURA, THE LEADER OF THE YADAVAS, CONFER

Krishna is painted brown, a rather unusual occurrence, as normally—and even in the other leaf of this series—he is colored blue. For a similar brown Krishna, see Archer, *Indian Miniatures,* pl. 64.

One other leaf from this series has been reproduced in the McNear catalog, no. 9.

41a KRISHNA, WITH ONE OF
HIS EIGHT QUEENS, SEATED WITH
THEIR DAUGHTER AND TEN SONS
Rajgarh (Malwa)

41b KRISHNA AND AKRURA,
THE LEADER OF THE YADAVAS, CONFER
Rajgarh (Malwa)

42 KRISHNA IN BATTLE WITH THE HORSE DEMON
From a *Bhagavata Purana* series.
Rajgarh (Malwa)
c. 1640
$6\frac{7}{8} \times 10\frac{1}{4}$

Another of the scourges of the forest of
Brindaban was a horse demon, who suddenly
appeared, pawing the ground and driving
away the herds. Krishna attacked him; and the
horse bit him and swallowed his arm. The
divine arm then grew to a gigantic size,
effectively splitting the demon apart (similar
treatment was also given to Bakasura the crane,
see no. 94). Here Krishna, attended by
cowherds, meets the monster. One of the
cowherds obligingly waves a peacock feather
fan to underline Krishna's royal lineage. The
horse in his excitement defecates a series
of ornamental orange and red spots.
This damaged miniature exhibits several
unusual features. Very short overskirts are
worn over dhotis of the usual kind. Such
overskirts occur very seldom in Indian pictures.
The central tree, one of a group of hyacinth-
shaped trees of a kind typical in Malwa
paintings, has a "leaning top"; and Krishna,
who usually appears blue, is painted white so
as not to disappear into the blue background of
the left half of the picture.

43 THE GODDESS CHANDI ATTACKS THE DEMON HOST
From a *Markandeya Purana* series.
Rajgarh (Malwa)
c. 1645
$5\frac{1}{2} \times 10$ (within borders)
The inscription on this miniature reads

maheshasura. The demon (*asura*) Mahesha appears as enemy of the goddess Durga in the episode of the *Mahesha-mardini* in which he is normally depicted as a buffalo demon. There is no chief demon here opposing the warrior goddess however. More frequent are depictions of Chandi, who here attacks a host of fiends with no specific leader. (For the attack of Chandi on a much more overflowing demon host, see Lee and Archer (1963), no. 54, from a later Guler series of which no. 86 is another example.)

Again, as in number 42, there is a slate blue background. The top and bottom panels of empty yellow, with pink borders, are seen again in nos. 45 a and b.

44 THE LEADERS OF THE MONKEY AND BEAR ARMIES
REPORT TO RAMA AFTER DISPATCHING A DEMON
From a *Ramayana* series.
Rajgarh (Malwa)
c. 1650
$6^7/_8$ x $6^1/_4$

In order to recover his wife, Sita, Rama lays siege to Lanka and is helped by the services of a monkey and bear army. Part of their military assignment is the decimation of the demon host of Ravana.

In this *Ramayana* series we see the use of a distinctive contrast of two colors: the flat, sumac color contrasted with a brilliant red (here used as background for Rama and the monkeys and bear). See also no. 45 a.

Other leaves from this series have been reproduced in Welch and Beach, fig. 12; and the Heeramaneck catalog, no. 153, p. 126.

44 THE LEADERS OF THE MONKEY AND BEAR ARMIES
REPORT TO RAMA AFTER DISPATCHING A DEMON
Rajgarh (Malwa)

45 Two leaves from a *Ragamala* series.
Rajgarh (Malwa)
c. 1650
8 x 6¾

a) ASAVARI RAGINI

Ex Coll.: Maharaja of Datia (Bundelkhand),
Central India.

Normally Asavari Ragini is a demure woman,
seated alone in a quiet landscape, surrounded by
the snakes that are her identifying feature.
Here, however, she appears on a brilliant red
background framed by the sumac color
mentioned above. She wears a peacock feather
headdress and skirt and is blue like Krishna.
This unusual color convention may suggest
her having smeared her body with ashes.

b) VARARI RAGINI

Varari appears with a more conventional
Malwa palette. The bereft lover is so
overwrought that he must be fanned by the
maid at his feet. The complicated patterns of
the numerous little turrets are set before a
plain black sky just as the pavilion is placed
before a plain wall.

The only leaf from this *Ragamala* series so far
reproduced is in McGregor, pl. V. Another leaf
is in the Heeramaneck collection.

46 THE LOVERS CONVERSE AS A GROUP OF LADIES
POUR WATER ON A FLOWERING BUSH
From a *Rasika Priya* series.
Rajgarh (Malwa)
c. 1655
$9\frac{1}{2} \times 7\frac{1}{4}$
A much more complicated scheme appears in
this picture than in the previous Malwa
pictures. The backgrounds are still completely
flat, but the use of separate registers is
expanded with the lotus pond at the bottom
and several rooms in the same building just
above it. The continuation of this convention
will culminate in most of the leaves of the
Bhagavata Purana series of c. 1720,
of which no. 48 is the most magnificent
example.

Other leaves from this series are in the
Heeramaneck and Binney collections.

47 MALASRI RAGINI From a *Ragamala* series.
Rajgarh (Malwa)
c. 1665
$7\frac{5}{8} \times 5\frac{1}{2}$
Exhibited: Persian and Indian Miniatures,
Binney Collection, West Coast Tour,
1962–64. Cat. no. 55.
The leaves from this *Ragamala* series feature a
distinctive band of scroll-like decoration at the
bottom which relates them to a group of
similar works with comparable patterns.
Several of these are cited below.

One leaf from this particular series from the
collection of the Cleveland Museum of Art,
has been reproduced in Lee. Other leaves are in
the Elterman and John Yeon collections.
Numerous Malwa pictures with analogous, if
slightly different, scrolls at the bottom, have
been reproduced. See particularly Ashton
(ed.), no. 425, pls. 84–85; Archer (1958), pl. 7;
Khajanchi catalog, no. 55 a, fig. 49; and
Barrett and Gray, p. 153.

46 THE LOVERS CONVERSE
AS A GROUP OF LADIES POUR WATER
ON FLOWERING BUSH
Rajgarh (Malwa)

48 KRISHNA DANCES WITH THE COWGIRLS
From a *Bhagavata Purana* series.
Narsinghgarh (Malwa)
c. 1720
$7^{15}/_{16} \times 14\frac{3}{4}$
The *Rasa Mandala* is the dance of Krishna with
the cowgirls, in which his all-pervading
presence is felt by each woman so completely
that she feels that he is dancing with her alone.
Here, not one, but two circles of dancers are
presented. In the circle on the left, Radha
dances with Krishna surrounded by the other
cowgirls. The right-hand circle shows the
more familiar portrayal of the duplicated
Krishna dancing with each woman.

The series was first mentioned in Archer
(1958), p. 12, note 2, where the presence of
ten leaves in the Victoria and Albert Museum,
London, was noted. Other leaves have been
reproduced in the McNear catalog, no. 12, and
the Sotheby auction catalog (June 27, 1967)
from which this miniature was purchased.
In addition to other leaves in the Archer and
Binney collections, examples are in the
collections of John D. MacDonald, Dr. Leland
Wyman, and an anonymous collector in
Cambridge, Massachusetts.

47 MALASRI RAGINI
Rajgarh (Malwa)

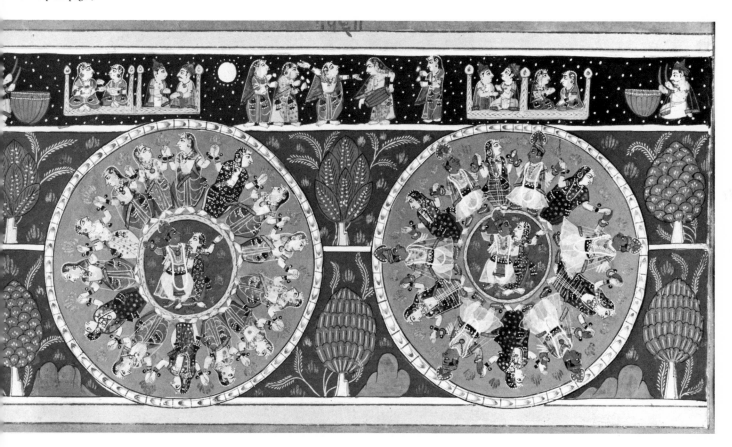

49 THE CONFIDANTE OF USHA,
DAUGHTER OF THE DEMON KING VANASURA,
CARRIES THE SLEEPING ANIRUDDHA,
GRANDSON OF KRISHNA, TO HER MISTRESS
Nepal
Color plate page 10

49 THE CONFIDANTE OF USHA, DAUGHTER OF THE
DEMON KING VANASURA, CARRIES THE SLEEPING
ANIRUDDHA, GRANDSON OF KRISHNA, TO
HER MISTRESS
From a *Bhagavata Purana* series.
Nepal, with strong Central Indian influence.
c. 1775
$14\frac{5}{8}$ x $21\frac{5}{8}$

The superimposed registers of earlier Malwa
painting have disappeared, and different rooms
in the castle (Krishna's palace) provide
simultaneous action. Krishna appears in the
lower left. His grandson Aniruddha is sleeping
in his bed in the center, but is being hoisted
aloft by Chitrekha, confidante of his bride-to-
be, Usha. She has dreamed of her future
husband, and Chitrekha has been sent to bring
him to her. She appears again with him in the
upper right prior to returning to her mistress.
The fish-filled river with the four boats and
the gorgeous star-studded sky frame the palace
compound with its feverish activity.

Leaves from this series were first published in
Oriental Bulletin no. 7 of Maggs Brothers,
London, which reproduced four of them and
listed several more. Two others, in Boston, are
reproduced in the *Bulletin* of the Boston
Museum of Fine Arts, vol. LXV (1967),
pp. 55-56. Besides other leaves in the Archer
and Binney collections, there are examples in
the Gahlin, Kanoria, MacDonald, and McNear
collections, and in the Victoria and Albert
Museum, London.

50 THE MAID ARRIVES TO CONDUCT A LOVER
TO HIS MISTRESS From a *Sat Saiya* series.
Datia (Bundelkhand)
c. 1750
$7\frac{1}{8}$ x $7\frac{3}{8}$

Ex Coll.: Maharaja of Datia (Bundelkhand),
Central India.

The *Sat Saiya* (1662), by the poet Bihari Lal,
presents another series of the states of lovers
like the *Rasika Priya* of Keshava Das (1581).
Although some of the couplets of the poem
are in praise of Krishna, other parts refer to
unidentified lovers.

The palette of the miniature (from which the
borders have been removed) is much more
subtle than that of a very similar series of the
Sat Saiya, also from Datia, leaves from which
have been reproduced in the Maggs Brothers'
Oriental Bulletin, no. 5, and in Welch and
Beach, no. 43. Other leaves from this later
series are in the Archer and Binney collections.

51 TODI RAGINI From a *Ragamala* series.
Central India

c. 1750

9 x 6 (within borders)

Exhibited: Persian and Indian Miniatures,
Binney Collection, West Coast Tour, 1962–64.
Cat. no. 80 (incorrectly assigned to Marwar).

Todi Ragini is often shown surrounded by
deer. Here, she plays a *vina,* a stringed
instrument with gourds which act as resonators.

52 GAURMALLAR RAGINI From a *Ragamala* series.
Central India.

c. 1750

11¾ x 8¾

Here again are the conventional treatments of
plants and landscape usual in the eastern group
of the Central Indian states: the trees whose
foliage is outlined against the skyline like a
long-handled fan; the banana, here hidden
behind another tree; the lotus pond in the
foreground; and the high rounded hillock.
Todi (no. 51) had only deer. Gaurmallar, who
also holds a *vina,* has five peacocks and pairs
of deer, monkeys, rabbits and flying cranes.

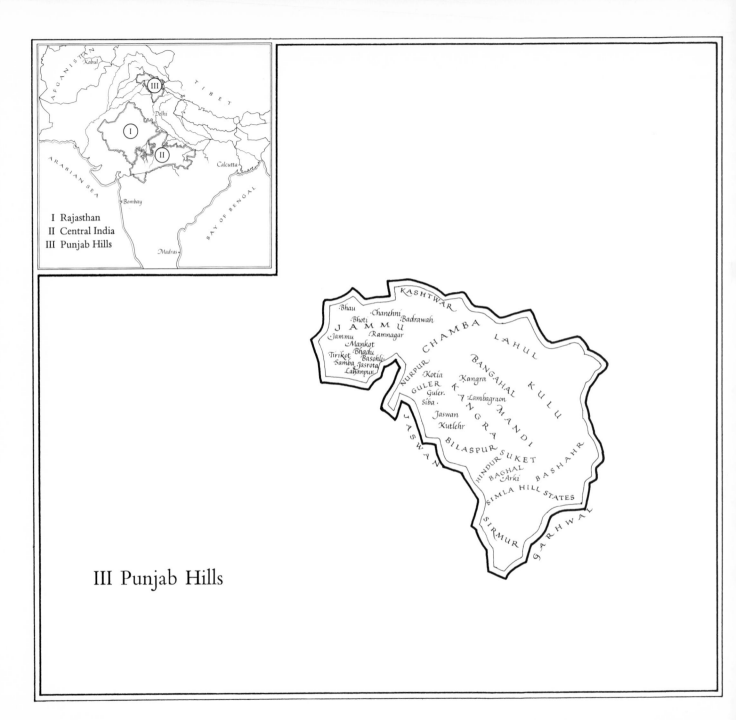

I Rajasthan
II Central India
III Punjab Hills

III Punjab Hills

III The Punjab Hills

The Punjab Hills were separated from Rajasthan by the Punjab Plains, a great corridor 300 miles long and 200 miles wide, which included at its southern end the imperial capital of Delhi. Bounded on the southwest by a low range of rough and stony hills, the region was 300 miles long and 100 miles wide. Unlike Rajasthan, with its burning deserts and rolling jungles, it consisted of a series of ascending foothills. Moderate slopes nearest the Plains were succeeded by enormous rounded hills, and these in turn were backed by the vast and towering Himalayas. The region included, in all, thirty-four states.

A first group, comprising barely one fifth of the entire region, is known as Jammu. Lying at the northwestern end of the Hills, it consisted of three parallel bands of states. Six—Lakhanpur, Jasrota, Samba, Tirikot, Dalpatpur, and Jammu itself—either adjoined or were near the Plains. Five—Basohli, Bhadu, Mankot, Bandralta (Ramnagar) and Bhoti—lay twenty or more miles further in. Finally, four others—Bhau, Chanehni, Bhadrawah, and Kashtwar—lay deep in the mountains. The area was bounded on the north by the river Tawi and on the south by the Ravi.

A second group was dominated by the vast state of Chamba and by its neighbor, the equally impressive Kangra. It included ten states—Nurpur, Guler, Kotla, Chamba, Siba, Datarpur, Kangra, Kutlehr, Jaswan, and Bangahal. Two of the five great Punjab rivers—the Ravi and the Beas—flowed through it, the Beas accounting for some of the lowest-lying portions in the Hills.

A third group involved nine states (excluding the Simla Hills) and accounted for almost half the total area. It comprised Kulu, Mandi, Suket, Bilaspur, Baghal, Hindur, Sirmur, Bashahr, and Garhwal. Of these, Kulu, Bashahr, and Garhwal lay deepest in the mountains, their huge hills making a formidable frontier.

MANKOT AND BASOHLI

Until the second half of the 17th century, none of the Rajput states in the Punjab Hills seem to have possessed any schools of local painting. Shortly after 1650, Mankot, a small state adjoining Basholi in the northwestern part of the area, developed a school of portraiture, and this was to last for almost a century. The subjects included Mankot rulers, palace servants and members of the Mankot court as well as neighboring rulers and their staffs. Important as a patron was Raja Mahipat Dev (c. 1660-c. 1690), whose burly figure with hooked nose was portrayed with simplified naturalism against deep yellow backgrounds. The style owed much to Mughal portraiture of the Shah Jahan period but was already Rajput in its use of flat planes, scorn of depth and perspective, and predilection for broad expanses of color. In about 1670 a daughter of Mahipat was married to Raja Kirpal Pal (ruled *c.* 1675-95) of Basohli. The marriage seems to have brought the two states into even closer conjunction, and between 1690 and 1700 one or more Basohli painters may have joined the Mankot court.

Until the reign of Kirpal Pal, Basohli, like Mankot, seems to have had no painting other than portraits in semi-Mughal style. Under this ruler a new style bursts on the scene. Its savage intensity and ardent colors suggest at first sight a close dependence on Mewar (Rajasthan). But there is no evidence of any direct links between the two states, and certain features of the new style—the use of suavely burnished surfaces, fragments of beetle-wing cases, flashing like emeralds, above all, a smooth barbaric magnificence—cause Mewar painting to seem, by contrast, rough and unsophisticated.

In its first phase of ordered ferocity, the new style seems to have lasted from about 1670 to 1690. It can be seen in one or more *Ragamalas,* a leaf from a *Bhagavata Purana,* and in pictures of Vishnu, Shiva and the latter's female counterpart, the Devi. Its most dazzling achievement, however, is a *Rasamanjari* of over one hundred pictures (preserved in great part in the Museum of Fine Arts, Boston, the Victoria and Albert Museum, and the Dogra Art Gallery, Jammu) where the ideal lovers of poetry are identified with Krishna.

This poem by Bhanu Datta seems to have had a special fascination for Kirpal Pal since, a year before his death in 1695, Devidasa (a painter from the adjoining state of Nurpur) executed for him a second version. Devidasa's style is in clear continuation of the great early manner, but he is already using larger and more rounded heads and slightly milder, less vehement eyes. Under Dhiraj Pal (1695-1722) and Medini Pal (1722-36) this tendency to milder expression continued. Stately compositions and a hot palette remained but figures as a whole became squatter and there was no longer the early rich variety. These traits characterize a *Gita Govinda* which was painted at Basohli in 1730 by yet another outside painter, Manaku of Guler. Guler and Basohli were already closely connected and the tie was strengthened by a double marriage when Govardhan Chand of Guler and Medini Pal of Basohli each married the other's sister.

The migration of Manaku from Guler, perhaps in 1725, was followed over the years by the arrival in Basohli of other members of his family, including his younger brother, Nainsukh. As a result of Dr. B. N. Goswamy's researches, it is now known that after working for fifteen years for the Jammu prince Balvant Singh, Nainsukh moved to Basohli in about 1760. Like his brother he must quickly have endeared himself to the Basohli royal family, for in 1763 Raja Amrit Pal of Basohli (reigned 1757-76) took him on pilgrimage to Hardwar. Here the painter immersed the ashes of his former Jammu patron in the Ganges. Much later, in 1778, Fattu, the first of Manaku's two sons, performed the same pious offices for his uncle Nainsukh and for Raja Amrit Pal himself.

Although Nainsukh and Fattu's activities at Basohli have still to be reconstructed in detail, the presence of these two artists may well account for a large *Bhagavata Purana* of about 1760-65, in which Guler and Basohli elements are clearly intermixed. This great series (no. 55 a-b) may have been executed in large part by Fattu with Nainsukh supervising the project or even at times assisting. Pictures showing Krishna with the milkmaids are closely dependent on similar scenes in Manaku's *Gita Govinda* of 1730, while their more muted color, greater naturalism, more complex compositions, and changes in facial types show Guler influence. A little later, perhaps between 1765 and 1770, the early style of Basohli was totally extinguished and its place was taken by a Guler variant. This Guler phase of Basohli painting lasted until about 1830 when the state came under the Sikhs.

Although after 1710 Basohli's role as a vital center of Rajput painting dwindled, the wild momentum of its first great phase seems to have led to vigorous offshoots in at least two other states—Mankot and Kulu. At Mankot the marriage of Mahipat Dev's daughter to Kirpal Pal readily accounts for a large number of pictures in Basohliesque style (formerly in the Mankot royal collection and now in the Chandigarh Museum). These pictures include a *Bhagavata Purana* with horizontal format as well as a variety of portraits which reveal Basohli influence in the greatly enlarged eyes and a far bolder use of color. In other respects, however, the local Mankot style persists. Rugs are severely rectangular with parallel stripes instead of being richly patterned. Backgrounds are starkly plain instead of full of detail. Above all, in sharp contrast to the aristocratic composure and high degree of control displayed in even the wildest of Basohli pictures, Mankot painting under Rajas Dhota Dev (*c.* 1690-*c.* 1700) and Tedhi Singh (*c.* 1700 - *c.* 1730) revels in violent dramatic movement and bounding rhythmical gestures. This sense of convulsive energy persists until at least 1720, and it is only under Raja Ajmat Dev (*c.* 1730 - *c.* 1760) that a style of stark simplicity blends with statuesque grace. Examples of this type of Mankot painting are two series formerly in the Lambagraon collection, Kangra. Following the extinction of the state in 1834, the Mankot family settled in Kutlehr, later a part of the British district of Kangra, and in the latter part of the 19th century provided Raja Sir Jai Chand of Lambagraon, Kangra with two princesses as brides. A *Bhagavata Purana* modelled on the earlier horizontal one but vertical in format and more summary in execution (no. 54 a-b) as well as illustrations of Hindu gods and goddesses (no. 53 a-b), all in strongly Mankot style, may have accompanied the princesses, thus accounting for their presence in the Lambagraon collection. Following the subjugation of Mankot by Jammu in about 1740, the local Mankot style was replaced by a variant of Jammu painting notable for its greater naturalism and its use of wan greys. Paintings in this sub-Jammu style continued to be produced at Mankot until the collapse of the Mankot court in 1834.

53a SHIVA AS
ARDHANARESHWARA
Mankot

53b THE KALKI
AVATAR OF VISHNU
Mankot

53 Two illustrations from different series of Hindu
deities.
Mankot

Ex Coll.: Raja Dhruv Dev Chand of
Lambagraon, Kangra, Punjab Hills

a) SHIVA AS ARDHANARESHWARA
c. 1720-30

$8\frac{5}{8}$ x $11\frac{1}{2}$

Shiva is presented here in androgenous form.

To the right, he is his usual male self; painted
white, a cobra around his neck, the third eye
in the middle of the forehead; he holds his
customary trident and is accompanied by his
vehicle, Nandi the bull. Grafted onto him is
his female counterpart, Uma or Kali. She wears
conventional female dress, holds a bowl which
is presumably full of blood (she is the goddess
of death), and is accompanied by her tiger.

b) THE KALKI AVATAR OF VISHNU
c. 1730-40

$8\frac{1}{2}$ x $11\frac{1}{2}$

Vishnu in his manifestation as Kalki, an armed
warrior who comes to rid the world of another
of its scourges. A worshipper is usually
portrayed in adoration before this avatar
of the god.

54 Two leaves from a *Bhagavata Purana* series.
Mankot

c. 1730-40

Ex Coll.: Raja Dhruv Dev Chand of
Lambagraon, Kangra, Punjab Hills.

a) THE EXCHANGE OF BABES

8¼ x 11¼

To save his life from a wicked kinsman
planning his murder, King Kansa, the
newborn Krishna was taken to the home of
Yasoda and Nanda, who thus become his
foster parents.

b) YASODA FEEDING THE YOUNG KRISHNA

8⅜ x 11½

Here Yasoda is shown feeding the boy
Krishna and his cowherd friends.

Other leaves from this series are reproduced
in Randhawa (1959), pl. 8-11 and 13. Other
leaves are in the Archer and Goenka collections,
and in the British Museum, London.

54b YASODA FEEDING THE YOUNG KRISHNA
Mankot

55 Two leaves from a *Bhagavata Purana* series.
Basohli
c. 1760-65
11 ¾ x 15 ¾

a) THE COWGIRLS ARE STUNNED BY KRISHNA'S
  DISAPPEARANCE

b) THE COWGIRLS GO IN SEARCH OF KRISHNA

These two consecutive episodes in the early
life story of Krishna show the reactions of the
cowgirls when they are confronted with the
loss of their friend. At first completely taken
aback by his disappearance, they shortly
thereafter try to find him by searching in the
forest.

Other leaves from this series are reproduced
in Binney (1962), no. 87; Lee and Archer,
no. 69; and Archer (1965), nos. 69, 71, and 72.
Other leaves are in art museums in Edinburgh,
London, and Cleveland and in the private
collections of Mildred and W. G. Archer,
Edwin Binney, Howard Hodgkin, Oliver
Skelton, Stuart Cary Welch, Mr. and Mrs.
W. P. Wood and various West Coast
collectors. A noteworthy group of great
artistic and esthetic importance is owned by
John D. MacDonald, Cambridge, Massachusetts.

55b THE COWGIRLS
GO IN SEARCH
OF KRISHNA
Basohli
Color plate page 11

75

The second state to be affected by Basohli painting was Kulu, a large area lying deep in the Himalayan mountains, one hundred miles to the east. A sister state of Basohli (the two families had common ancestors), it was well qualified to profit from Basohli developments. In about 1650, the Kulu Raja had vested his royal powers in Raghunath, an image of Rama, and from then onwards had ruled as the god's deputy. Under Raja Man Singh (1688-1719), Kulu had greatly prospered and as part of celebrations in honor of Raghunath, painters from Basohli may have gone to Kulu to prepare a large *Ramayana*. The series, at one time comprising 270 leaves, is known as the "Shangri" *Ramayana*—from Shangri, the place where a branch of the Kulu royal family, formerly possessing the pictures, settled in the 19th century. Although the series is in four distinct styles, it is remarkable for the skill with which a plethora of Basohli idioms and details have been put to fresh use and given a new and haunting flavor. Kulu, with its weird landscape, swirling mists, and clumsy villagers, is the very reverse of Basohli which is snugly situated near the Punjab Plains. Style I (no. 56 a-b) employs twisted physiques, heavy jowls, straggling locks of hair, eerily gazing eyes, and an air of frantic disruption which matches the wildness of the Kulu countryside. Style II (no. 57) is notable for golden yellow backgrounds, figures with beaked noses and jangled stances. Style III (no. 58) is naively exuberant and Style IV (no. 71) also deviates from the Basohli norm. This latter style is perhaps an adjustment to Kulu conditions by a painter from Bilaspur. A striking extension of Style I is a richly turbulent *Ragamala* (no. 59), also of the Man Singh period.

Under Man Singh's successor Raj Singh (1717-31), the farouche distortions of Style I are continued, but the glowing richness and grandeur of color, typical of

Styles I, II and III are discarded in favor of more sombre and paler hues, seen at times in Style IV. Backgrounds range from black or dark brown to pale yellow or sage green though details of costume provide extraordinary modulations of rich and subtle color. A striking example is no. 60 where a Kulu lady in slate-blue dress with blackish-purple veil, a red flower lighting up, like a match, her scarlet lips, is set against a light green background. The conjunction of pale setting with poetic costume and flashing color renders magically sinister her typically receding brow and coolly calculating eyes.

Until about 1740 (no. 61), Style I of the "Shangri" *Ramayana* continued to dominate painting in Kulu, its blend of nervous sophistication and towering majesty reflecting the ghostly and tormented character of the Kulu landscape. From 1740 to 1770, a slackening of expression occurs, but the introduction of huge spear-shaped pine trees into pictures shows that the landscape was still a vital factor. In 1767 Raja Pritham Singh came to the throne, and during the next forty years, ending with his death in 1806, a new style emerged. Unlike previous painting in Kulu, it relied on harshly geometric compositions (no. 62), but its use of dark red, green, and blue for dresses harks back to Style I, while the prevalence of pale backgrounds suggests that even Style IV was still exerting a diluted influence. Between 1790 and 1800, three sets of pictures are inscribed with the name of a painter Bhagvan, two of them dated 1794 and 1799. Although the Kulu capital was named Sultanpur, the place of origin is in two cases called Raghunathpur, "the city of Raghunath," a circumstance which proves how mindful of the Kulu deity's presence were Raja, court, and painters and how implicit in Kulu painting was a sense of the supernatural.

56a THE SUPERCESSION
OF RAMA
Kulu
Color plate page 12

56 Two leaves from the "Shangri" *Ramayana*,
Part II, the *Ayodhya Kanda*.
Style I.
Kulu
c. 1690-1710

Ex Coll.: Raja Raghbir Singh of Shangri in
the Kulu Valley, Punjab Hills.

a) THE SUPERCESSION OF RAMA

8½ x 12

The enfeebled King Dasaratha reclines on a rug
while his consort induces him to reverse his
decision to appoint Rama as co-regent. Rama,
accompanied by Lakshmana and Sita with her
maids, expresses his loyalty by the joining
of his hands.

b) RAMA BIDS FAREWELL

8⅝ x 12½

Rama, still accompanied by Lakshmana and
Sita, bows before King Dasaratha, preparatory
to leaving for exile in his waiting chariot.
The king places his right hand on the head of
Rama, as he kneels before him.

Other leaves from this series have been
reproduced in Randhawa (1959), pls. 16 and
18; and the Heeramaneck catalog, no. 178,
p. 135. Other leaves are in the National Museum,
New Delhi; Bharata Kala Bhavan, Banaras; the
British Museum, and Victoria and Albert
Museum, London, and the Kanoria and
Binney collections.

57 THE WEDDING GUESTS ASSEMBLE

From the "Shangri" *Ramayana,* Part I, the
Bala Kanda. Style II.

Kulu

c. 1690–1710

9 x 12⅞

Ex Coll.: Raja Raghbir Singh of Shangri in
the Kulu Valley, Punjab Hills.

Raja Dasaratha, king of Ayodhya,
accompanied by his four sons—Rama,
Lakshmana, Bharata, and Satrughna—arrives at
the palace of Raja Janaka, King of Mithila, to
ratify the marriages of Rama and Lakshmana
to Raja Janaka's two daughters and to negotiate
the marriages of his two remaining sons to Raja
Janaka's two nieces.

Rama and Lakshmana, armed with bows and
arrows, sit with a group of armed retainers in
the left foreground. Their hosts appear from
the right, the king under one umbrella which
balances another umbrella shading the royal
guests who sit at the rear of the balustraded
terrace.

No leaves from this style of the "Shangri"
Ramayana have so far been reproduced. Other
leaves are in the National Museum, New
Delhi; Bharat Kala Bhavan, Banaras; and the
Binney collection.

58 THE MONKEYS CONFER
From the "Shangri" *Ramayana,* Part IV, the
Kishkindha Kanda. Style III.
Kulu
c. 1700-10
7¾ x 11¼
Ex Coll.: Raja Raghbir Singh of Shangri in
the Kulu Valley, Punjab Hills.
Exhibited: Persian and Indian Miniatures,

Binney Collection, West Coast Tour, 1962-64.
Cat. no. 81.

During the quest for Sita, the leaders of the
monkey armies meet under a great tree with an
emissary of the bear army. Style III of this
Ramayana is used mainly for scenes showing the
monkey armies.

Other leaves from this style of the "Shangri"

Ramayana have been reproduced in Skelton,
pls. 39 and 40. Other leaves are in the National
Museum, New Delhi; Bharat Kala Bhavan,
Banaras; and the Binney and Heeramaneck
collections.

59 KAMODINI
RAGINI
Kulu
Color plate page 13

59 KAMODINI RAGINI From a *Ragamala* series.
Kulu
c. 1700-10
6¼ x 6¼ (trimmed)
Ex Coll.: Howard Hodgkin.
Other examples from this grand and wild series
are in the Victoria and Albert Museum, London,
and the Museum of Fine Arts, Boston
(Coomaraswamy [1926], pl. 32).

60 A KULU LADY SEATED ON A STRIPED RUG
HOLDING A FLOWER
Kulu
c. 1720
7¹³⁄₁₆ x 4½
Portraits of Pahari noblemen and ladies often
show their sitters on striped rugs. The
rugs are presented as though seen from above
while the sitter is seen from shoulder height.
Unusual about this lady is the complete edge
of her ear pierced to receive a series of true
ear-rings (as opposed to the usual ear-*lobe*-rings)
and her cloak with the narrow band across her
upper body. (The goddess Lakshmi wears a
similar cloak in no. 61.)

61 VISHNU AND LAKSHMI SEATED TOGETHER
ON A LOTUS
Kulu
c. 1740
7½ x 5¾ (irregular)
When Vishnu appears with his consort, it is
called *Lakshminarayana*. His four arms grasp
his usual attributes—mace, discus, lotus flower,
and conch shell. Lakshmi clasps her henna-
stained hands together in adoration.
The primary colors of Kulu painting are all
displayed here—the flat yellow of the
background, the strong reds and blues of the
clothes of the divine couple. Strength replaces
subtlety, but the almost frantic intensity of the
earlier ragini (no. 59) has gone.

60 A KULU LADY SEATED ON
A STRIPED RUG HOLDING A FLOWER
Kulu

61 VISHNU
AND LAKSHMI
SEATED TOGETHER
ON A LOTUS
Kulu

62 THE RELUCTANT RADHA

Kulu

c. 1770–80

9¼ x 6⅛

Radha, seated on a terrace with Krishna, seems unconvinced about her eventual surrender, although two of her maids stand beside the waiting bed. The chevron-shaped decoration on the side pillar and roof of their bedroom is mirrored in the supports of the domed pavilion. Their color and shape stem from the displayed architectural lotus which serves as finial of the dome. Beyond the garden railing is a flowering cypress which heralds the complexities of later vegetation in Punjab Hill miniatures. A flight of birds ascends the night sky.

Like other states further to the northwest, Mandi, Bilaspur, and Baghal (also known as Arki from the name of its capital) appear to have had no schools of painting until the second half of the 17th century. In about 1680 Mandi, a bitter rival of Kulu, developed a cumbersome variant of Shah Jahan-style Mughal portraiture. Mughal emperors such as Jahangir (no. 63) and local Mandi rajas and princes (nos. 65 and 67) were painted with over-large heads in a simple palette of white, slate-blue, green, and brown. Mughal ladies of the 17th century also seem to have provided models for female types—Mandi artists once again painting them with a rough bucolic coarseness far removed from the delicacy of their distant originals. In many portraits, rows of birds in flight, a detail borrowed from Mughal painting in the Deccan, were also introduced. In 1722, Raja Shiva Jawala Sen predeceased his father, the nonogenarian giant, Sidh Sen (1684-1727). He is shown (no. 65) riding a lumbering cart horse with a member of his escort bearing a great flapping banner before him. The gross exaggerations and stumbling crudity of style are in sharp contrast to the wild but brilliantly intricate painting of Kulu. Besides portraying rajas and their companions, painters in Mandi also concentrated on studies of Shiva (by far the most widely worshipped deity in the state) and also, though to a much smaller extent, on scenes from the *Ramayana* (no. 66) and *Bhagavata Purana*. The latter text described the actions of Madho Rai (Krishna the flute-player) to whom the state had been dedicated by Raja Suraj Sen (1637-54). The flute-playing god seems, however, to have been far less successful in safeguarding Mandi interests than his rival, Raghunath, in Kulu, and to judge from the comparative rarity of Mandi pictures dealing with Krishna, popular interest in his cult was correspondingly slight.

In 1793, the young Raja Isvari Sen (1788-1826) was abducted by his powerful neighbor, Raja Sansar Chand (1775-1823) of Kangra and was compelled to spend twelve inglorious years as captive at his court. His father, Shamsher Sen (no. 67), had married a Guler princess and it is possible that on Isvari Sen's release in 1805, following the invasion of Kangra by the Gurkhas, he installed a Guler painter, Sajnu, at his court. In 1810, Sajnu completed a *Hamir Hath* series which told the story of an overproud ruler's downfall—perhaps an oblique reference to the hated Sansar Chand. He also presented his royal patron with three pictures dated 1808, one of them showing Raja Isvari Sen worshipping Shiva and his consort Parvati. Sajnu's style (no. 68) is in total contrast to the "country bumpkin" character of Mandi painting in the 18th century and instead reflects the sensitive elegance of Guler pictures of the 1750 to 1780 period. Apart from its delicate smoothness, a feature of Sajnu's style is his fondness for jagged shapes, pale color and angular rhythms—characteristics which are also reflected in the work of his assistants and followers (no. 69).

Bilaspur, a small but powerful state adjoining Mandi on the south, began by following a somewhat similar course and in the second half of the 17th century developed its own variant of Shah Jahan-style portraiture. Facial types bore significant resemblance to Mughal prototypes, but novel Bilaspur details were long and wriggling side curls and markedly dwindled lower limbs. In contrast to Mandi practice, faces were sensitively rendered, and at times an air of royal grandeur was conveyed through costumes richly patterned with floral sprigs. As at Mandi, white, green, and brown (but not slate-blue) were favorite colors to which orange and olive were sometimes added. Under Rajas Dip Chand (1650-67) and Bhim Chand (1667-1712), these colors provide a basic norm for royal portraits and for many *Ragamalas* (nos. 70 a-b).

Under Raja Ajmer Chand (reigned 1712-41 but actual ruler of Bilaspur from 1692) religious subjects begin to intrude and the color red is also used with assertive boldness. A portrait of Ajmer Chand, now in the Victoria and Albert Museum but formerly in one of the two Bilaspur ancestral collections, shows him standing against a sage-green background, clad in a long red skirt, and worshipping Rama and Sita. His devotion to Rama may also explain the presence in Kulu of a Bilaspur painter (no. 71) at the time when the "Shangri" *Ramayana* was being painted (1690-1710). Ajmer Chand was on friendly terms with Man Singh of Kulu, and he may well have deputed a painter to assist in the project. The latter's contribution to the series may account for Style IV, in which Bilaspur idioms are given an unusual Kulu bias.

Under Raja Devi Chand (1741-78), Bilaspur prospered and, amongst other developments, the cult of Krishna received belated recognition. Devi Chand had married a Kangra princess, and although her difficult personality later led to a complete breakdown in relations between the two states, her involvement in the cult may explain its celebration in Bilaspur painting between 1770 and 1800. Salient characteristics of late Bilaspur painting are trees with gouged-out holes, hard and brusque compositions, and figures with Guler-type faces.

The state of Baghal (capital, Arki) was largely dependent on Bilaspur, but in the course of the 18th century developed a minor variant of the Bilaspur style. Its painting was notable for hesitant meandering compositions, rulers with thickly braided locks of hair (no. 75), and for lovers tweaking their mistresses' persons or brusquely clutching at their veils.

63 PORTRAIT OF THE MUGHAL EMPEROR JAHANGIR
(ruled 1605-1627)
Mandi
c.1660-80
10⁷⁄₈ x 6⁷⁄₈
The Pahari rajas were not unnaturally
interested in their Mughal overlords and

occasionally commissioned sets of portraits of
them. It is amusing to compare this coarse,
almost caricatural, picture with the known
character of the sitter. Jahangir was the most
esthetically knowledgeable of all the Mughal
emperors and possessed an almost infallible
"eye" in the appreciating and cataloging of
the miniatures and manuscripts of his own
extensive collection.

64 THE GOD BRAHMA SEATED ON A SARAS CRANE
Mandi
c. 1710
7³⁄₄ x 7³⁄₁₆
Brahma, the premier god of the Hindu trinity,
is normally portrayed as accompanied by, or
astride, a goose, which is his vehicle, as Garuda
is Vishnu's and Nandi the bull Shiva's. Here,
however, he rides a saras crane.

64 THE GOD BRAHMA
SEATED ON A SARAS CRANE
Mandi

63 PORTRAIT OF
THE MUGHAL EMPEROR JAHANGIR
Mandi

65 A MANDI PRINCE, PERHAPS SHIVA JAWALA SEN
(d. 1722), RIDING WITH AN ESCORT
Mandi
c. 1710
8 x 11½ (badly worn at the side edges)
The ruling family of Mandi used "Sen" as the
last part of the name of all its rulers. Basohli
similarly used "Pal," Chamba "Singh," and
Jammu "Dev," while Bilaspur, Guler, and
Kangra all favored "Chand." Shiva Jawala
predeceased his father, Raja Sidh Sen of Mandi
and never ruled. He is here portrayed in a
simple, coarse, group portrait, looking strongly
like his son, Raja Sham Sher Sen (no. 67).

66 RAVANA IN BATTLE WITH RAMA AND
LAKSHMANA WHILE THE RESCUED SITA STANDS
BETWEEN THE BROTHERS
From a *Ramayana* series.
Mandi
c. 1750
5⅜ x 7⅞ (irregular)
Exhibited: Persian and Indian Miniatures,
Binney Collection, West Coast Tour, 1962-64.
Cat. no. 83.
The many-headed and many-armed Ravana,
demon king of Lanka, is shown in battle with
Rama and Lakshmana. They have enlisted
the aid of monkey and bear armies to recapture

Sita, Rama's wife, whom Ravana has abducted. The demon king, his braying ass-head thrusting upwards from among his human heads, seems surprisingly alone with only two small demons in front of him and two solitary archers behind. But the monkeys who cross the moat of the castle of Lanka are unarmed, and the bears in the foreground seem very small. Rama has already rescued Sita, but Ravana's nineteen arms which are here shown with a complete arsenal of hand weapons, will inflict a frightful carnage.

67 RAJA SHAM SHER SEN OF MANDI (ruled 1727-81), SEATED — SMOKING A HOOKAH
Mandi
c. 1780
$11\frac{1}{8} \times 8$

The raja is relaxing. Gazing blankly into the distance (as are his two attendants), he has untied the triangular lapel of his robe and is nonchalantly fingering the garland, which resembles a Hawaiian lei, around his neck. Mandi painting has been evolving. There is a definite attempt to leave behind the rustic look of previous pictures (cf. no. 66). The pattern of the rugs is somewhat more sophisticated. A master painter will completely transform the pictorial tradition of the state in the near future (nos. 68 and 69).

67 RAJA SHAM SHER SEN
OF MANDI, SEATED,
SMOKING A HOOKAH
Mandi

68 A GATHERING STORM
Mandi,
style of Sajnu

68 A GATHERING STORM
Mandi, style of Sajnu
c. 1820

8¼ x 4½ (within black borders)

The lady on the terrace feels completely alone despite the presence of her four maids. She has donned her loveliest clothes and has dyed her palms (and no doubt the soles of her feet) with henna, but her lover has not come. The storm which is soon to unleash its fury reflects her own unease. And in the distance, along the banks of the river, each bird has found a mate. The Guler painter Sajnu has appeared in Mandi and completed the transformation of its pictorial traditions. This picture is closer to the master than the following catalog entry, which is more probably by one of his followers.

Compare Archer, *Indian Miniatures,* pl. 94, since assigned to Mandi and dated c. 1820.

69 THE HOLY FAMILY

Mandi, school of Sajnu

c. 1830

9¾ x 7¾

Shiva and his family are resting in the
mountains on the skin of a huge elephant
which he has killed. Each of the members of
the family has his vehicle in close attendance.
Nandi the bull, who is Shiva's, rests in the
lower right, his huge "Brahma bull" hump
freed from his saddle cloth. The sleeping tiger
belongs to Durga, a manifestation of Shiva's
wife, Parvati, who sits beside her lord. She is
holding their son, the many-headed
Kartikkeya, god of war. His vehicle, the
peacock, is perched in the tree above their
heads. Ganesha (see no. 38), their other son,
sleeps in front of his father. His vehicle, the
rat, remains on the alert at the left, his
oversized tail parallel to the tail of the
elephant skin.

The oval shape of the central group, marked
by the elephant's trunk, Nandi's hump and
neck, the back of the sleeping tiger, and the
tails of the rat and elephant, is starkly broken
by the dark triangle of the cave in front of
which they are resting.

70 Two leaves from a *Ragamala* series.
Bilaspur
c. 1685-90

a) PUNYAKI RAGINI, WIFE OF BHAIRAVA RAGA
10 x 8¾

Punyaki Ragini can be recognized because she
is giving alms to begging gurus. The unusual,
wild colors—so different from the palettes of
the other contemporary Hill States—are
nowhere more distinctive than here: the
flaming yellow of the borders, the strong, yet
pale violet, and the vibrant red. The sickly
green of the trees completes a very disquieting
color range.

b) VIGADA (or Vahagada, or Vehagada) RAGA,
SON OF SRI RAGA

10⅛ x 7¹¹⁄₁₆

Vigada seems mild by comparison with the
ragini; the brown background and the figured
pale yellow rug seem hardly to belong to the
same series, but identical borders and the
facial types conforming to the same pattern
belie the dissimilar palettes.

No leaves from this series have been so far
reproduced, but a leaf in the Heeramaneck
collection is noted in the Heeramaneck
catalog, no. 182, where, however, it is
unidentified and misdated. The Binney
collection has a third leaf (Vasanta Raga, son
of Hindola Raga).

70b VIGADA RAGA,
SON OF SRI RAGA
Bilaspur

71 RAMA AND LAKSHMANA APPROACHING
THE DEAD MULES From the "Shangri"
Ramayana, Part II, the *Aranya Kanda.* Style IV.
By a Bilaspur artist working in Kulu.
c. 1700-10

8½ x 12¼

Ex Coll.: Raja Raghbir Singh of Shangri in
the Kulu Valley, Punjab Hills.

Rama and Lakshmana, in quest of Rama's
wife Sita, come upon a heap of four dead
mules, slaughtered by their ally Jataya, king
of the vultures, while destroying Ravana's
chariot.

In this picture, the "Shangri" *Ramayana*
appears in its fourth style (see nos. 56-58).
The Kulu attribution is obvious, the profiles
with the distinctive noses being already present
in Style II (no. 57); but the palette has changed.
The very pale yellow backgrounds are
common only to this part of the series. (The
text continued around the border is also usual
to this part of the "Shangri" set.) The fact
that a Bilaspur artist working at Kulu painted
this part of the set explains its present inclusion
under Bilaspur. Note the complex rhythms of
the pile of dead mules, their bright saddles
dotted through the irregular heap.

One leaf from this style of the "Shangri"
Ramayana has been reproduced in Khandalavala,
no. 42. Other leaves are in the National
Museum, New Delhi; the Binney collection;
and several West Coast private collections.

71 RAMA AND LAKSHMANA APPROACHING THE DEAD MULES Kulu

94

72 KRISHNA EMERGES FROM THE JAMUNA RIDING
ON THE SNAKE DEMON KALIYA
Bilaspur.
c. 1710
9½ x 6½
Exhibited: Persian and Indian Miniatures,
Binney Collection, West Coast Tour, 1962-64.
Cat. no. 86 (mistakenly assigned to Guler).

The *Kaliya Damana,* the contest between
Krishna and the snake demon who has
terrorized the region along the banks of the
Jamuna River, has ended. Krishna has defeated
the monster, but before the loser is exiled, the
victor rides on his conquered opponent.

73 SHIVA AND PARVATI ON MOUNT KAILASA
Bilaspur
c. 1720
8½ x 8⅛
Exhibited: Persian and Indian Miniatures,
Binney Collection, Portland Supplementary
Exhibition. Cat. no. 83a (mistakenly assigned
to Kulu).

The lord Shiva is meditating as a naked ascetic
on a peak in the Himalayas. He pays no
attention to Parvati, who presents him with a
cup, nor to the devout worshipper below, nor
to Nandi his bull vehicle who waits under the
mountain. The river Ganges can be seen
faintly, springing from Shiva's hair to start its
mighty course to the sea under the feet of the
male devotee (cf. nos. 37 and 38). The pale
colors are a change from the feverishness of
early miniatures from other Hill States.

74 BALARAMA DIVERTS
THE CHANNEL OF THE JAMUNA RIVER
WITH HIS PLOUGHSHARE
TO PROVIDE A BATHING PLACE
Bilaspur

74 BALARAMA DIVERTS THE CHANNEL OF THE
JAMUNA RIVER WITH HIS PLOUGHSHARE TO
PROVIDE A BATHING PLACE
From a *Bhagavata Purana* series.
Bilaspur
c. 1730-40
7½ x 9⅞
Ex Coll.: Hagop Kevorkian.
While Balarama begins his task of making a
suitable swimming place, his brother Krishna
converses with a friend. The varied shades of
red in the miniature itself—from orange
through brick to rust—are surrounded by still
another red in the border. The deep flat green
of the background serves as foil for them all.

75 RANA MEHR CHAND OF BAGHAL (ARKI) SEATED
SMOKING WITH JAI SINGH OF KULU WHO
HOLDS A HAWK
Baghal (Arki)
c. 1720
7³⁄₁₆ x 10¾
Exhibited: Persian and Indian Miniatures,
Binney Collection, Portland Supplementary
Exhibition, Cat. no. 81 b (mistakenly assigned
to Basohli).
Pictures from the state of Baghal, whose
capital town is Arki, show the same weak
colors as the miniature from Bilaspur (no. 73).
The workmanship here is also hesitant.
A portrait of Jai Singh with Devi Chand of
Bilaspur is reproduced in Skelton, pl. 61.
Rana Mehr Chand ruled 1727-41. Jai Singh of
Kulu ruled 1731-42. Both are here depicted
as princes.

97

The state of Nurpur lies east of Basohli, south of Chamba, and west of Guler. Under Raja Jagat Singh (1618-46) it terrorized its neighbors and for a time was the strongest power in the Punjab Hills. Later in the 17th century it lost its dominant position and was of minor importance.

Although few early paintings have survived, it is likely that in the later years of Raja Man Dhata (1661-1700) Nurpur artists were already practising a style similar to that of Mankot and Basohli, though lacking the latter's polished assurance. Devidasa, who painted the Basohli *Rasamanjari* of 1694, came from Nurpur and the reputation of his son, Golu, was so legendary that an annual fair named after him is still held at Nurpur today. The family's link with Basohli was important since a *Rasamanjari* (no. 76 a and b), obviously based in essentials on Devidasa's Basohli series, was painted at Nurpur in about 1720. The style is in every way cooler than the hot and fierce Basohli manner; the colors pink, mauve and slate-blue are often used; features are no longer exaggerated; and it is only in the writhing contortions of the ladies' veils that a touch of "romantic agony" is apparent. Although Nurpur was a prominent center of the Krishna cult, the *Rasamanjari* of 1720 portrays the hero, or ideal lover, as Krishna only when the verses of the original actually require it. For the rest, in contrast to standard Basohli practice, the lover is modelled on the local raja, Daya Dhata (1700-35). Despite this glorification of the ruler—a practice current in Rajasthan —Krishna subjects were by no means neglected and although only one leaf (no. 77) of a *Bhagavata Purana* appears to have survived, its entire tenth and eleventh books could well have been illustrated at Nurpur at about this time. Golu himself is credited with painting a large mural in the Krishna shrine within the Nurpur fort. Besides poetic and Vaishnava subjects, *Ragamalas* were also produced—no. 78 coming from a series closely related in style to the *Rasamanjari,* but possibly painted ten to twenty years later.

Although the genealogy of Daya Dhata's family is still controversial, it is likely that he was succeeded first by Raja Fateh Singh (c. 1735-c. 1770) and then by Pirthi Singh (c. 1770-1805). Under Fateh Singh, Nurpur painters adopted a darker, richer palette, reduced the scale of their subjects, elongated the figures and gave them keener features (no. 79). Under Pirthi Singh, the vogue for tall female figures with high waists was probably continued, and situations involving either Krishna or ideal lovers were interpreted in dark reds and blues against stark and simple settings (no. 80 a and b). Under Raja Bir Singh (1805-46), Nurpur came quickly under Sikh control, the raja becoming a hapless refugee. He had been earlier married to a sister of Raja Charat Singh of Chamba and was granted asylum at that court. His residence there may explain occasional Nurpur elements in Chamba painting of the early 19th century.

In contrast to Nurpur, a small state abutting on the Punjab Plains, Chamba was larger than Kulu and lay even further in the mountains. In the late 17th century, a style of portraiture similar to that of Mankot seems to have prevailed, but this was probably superseded by a more Basohli-like manner between about the years 1710 and 1735. As in Nurpur, the rich magnificence of the Basohli style was eschewed, but mannerisms such as receding foreheads and geometrical rosettes for trees were quietly adopted. Like its neighbor Kangra, Chamba included in its population groups of Gaddis—a shepherd caste which frequented the higher hills and was regarded by its Rajput neighbors as quaint oddities. A picture (no. 81) illustrating this point of view and perhaps executed in 1730 is included in the exhibition. Under Raja Umed Singh (1748-64), versions of the *Ramayana* and *Bhagavata Purana* were produced—a minor painter, Laharu, contributing a leaf to one of them at the instance of a certain Mian Shamsher Singh in 1757. Nos. 82 and 83 with their reticent distortions and pale colors illustrate the style of Laharu's master and his associates.

Under Raja Raj Singh (1764-94), Chamba painting enters a vitally new stage. In about 1770, the sister of Raj Singh was married to Prakash Chand of Guler (ruled 1773-90, died 1820), and perhaps as a by-product of the marriage, the Guler artist Nikka was invited to join the Chamba court. Nikka was third son of Nainsukh, the Guler painter who had worked first in Jammu and then in Basohli. No inscribed examples of his work at Chamba are known, but portraits of Raj Singh and his family reveal a sharp break with former traditions and a strong influx of Guler idioms. The facial type which was adopted by Kangra from Guler practice became current and there is a new response to feminine charm. It is reasonable to suppose that Nikka was responsible for these changes. A second generation of immigrants, represented by Nikka's sons, the artists Harkhu and Chajju, accounts for further Guler influences in the 1800 to 1830 period, while yet another painter, Tara Singh, may have acclimatized a mixed Guler-Garhwal style at Chamba in the years 1840 to 1860.

76 Two leaves from a *Rasamanjari* series.
Nurpur
c. 1720

a) A NEGLECTED LOVER WAITS ALONE

6½ x 10½

Exhibited: Persian and Indian Miniatures,
Binney Collection, Portland Supplementary
Exhibition. Cat no. 82a (mistakenly assigned
to Basohli).

b) THE NEGLECTED MISTRESS CONFIDES
IN A FRIEND

6⅞ x 10⅜

Exhibited: Persian and Indian Miniatures,
Binney Collection, West Coast Tour, 1962-64.
Cat. no. 82 (mistakenly assigned to Basohli).

The *Rasamanjari* of the poet Bhannu Datta
codifies the types of lovers, whether alone or
in couples. Nurpur painting, unlike that of
other states, is typified by a male face
with an excessively long vertical axis. Here this
length is enhanced by the distinctive turban
which continues the line of the face. The face
strongly resembles that of Raja Daya Dhata
(c. 1700-35) (cf. no. 77).

Leaves from this series have been reproduced
in Ashton (ed.), nos. 513 and 514, pls. 97-99;
Khandalavala and M. Chandra, *Lalit Kala,* no. 3,
p. 30 and pls. 6 and 7; Khandalavala, fig. 62
and nos. 25, 28-30; Archer, *Indian Miniatures,*
pl. 72; Barrett and Gray, p. 168. Other leaves
are in the British Museum, London, and the
Archer, Bickford, Heeramaneck, and Lee
collections.

77 THE FINAL BATTLE From a *Bhagavata Purana* series.
Nurpur
c. 1720
$6\frac{1}{2}$ x $10\frac{1}{8}$

The battle of the Yadavas among themselves appears at the end of the eleventh book of the *Bhagavata Purana*. Profuse spurts of blood obscure the frenetic pattern of the intermingled bodies. The long Nurpur face mentioned above is seen on the combatant in the upper right who is flailing a dying enemy with whips held in both hands. Others of the faces are also long, but not as long as that of this warrior.

77 THE FINAL BATTLE
Nurpur

78 KARNATI RAGINI (wife of Sri Raga). From a
Ragamala series.
Nurpur
c. 1730-40
8¾ x 7¼
The female face here is strongly reminiscent
of the earlier *Rasamanjari* series (cf. no. 76 b).
The *takri* characters of the inscription at the
top describe the subject as *ragini bangali,* an
incorrect identification, as Bangali has an
accompanying lion.
For the reproduction of a leaf from a Nurpur
Ragamala series in similar style, and for a
Bilaspur version of Karnati Ragini, see
Waldschmidt, pl. A and fig. 50.

79 VIEWING OF THE NEW MOON
Nurpur
c. 1750
9¼ x 6³⁄₁₆
A raja with five of his women has gone
outside to look at the crescent of the new
moon. A servant accompanies him with a
hookah pipe. The elegant long waists of both
the female and the male dress are outlined by
the plain green landscape.

78 ARNATI RAGINI,
WIFE OF SRI RAGA
Nurpur

80 Two leaves from a *Nayaka-Nayika* series.
Nurpur

c. 1770

a) VIPRALABDHA NAYIKA

7⁷⁄₈ x 5³⁄₄

Vipralabdha is the jilted lady who, after vainly
searching for her lover, realizes that
he will not come. Overheated by her
unassuaged desire, she casts off her armlets.

b) UTKA NAYIKA

7¹¹⁄₁₆ x 5⁹⁄₁₆

Utka does not know whether her lover will
come. She stands alone in the forest waiting
for him.

The *Nayaka-Nayika Bheda* classifies the types
of lovers, as does the *Rasamanjari* (cf. nos.
76 a and b). The contrast of the pale and dark
skies behind the two lonely women is striking.

80a VIPRALABDHA NAYIKA
Nurpur

80b UTKA NAYIKA
Nurpur

81 THREE GADDIS, ONE OF THEM DRESSED AS
KRISHNA, SINGING TO THE ACCOMPANIMENT OF
A TAMBOURINE AND CLAPPERS
Chamba
c. 1730
5½ x 7½

The *gaddis* are shepherds who inhabit the
mountainous uplands of several of the Punjab
Hill states. They are unlettered and somewhat
uncouth and are usually caricatured with some
malice. The profiles with the high-bridged
noses, and the short skirts which end at
mid-thigh are not found among other
Hill groups.
Another picture of *gaddis* is reproduced in
Khandalavala, fig. 7. It shows the skirts and a
similar but two-pointed "dunce cap." The
facial type appears in the left hand figure
in Skelton, pl. 42.

81 THREE GADDIS, ONE OF THEM DRESSED AS KRISHNA, SINGING
TO THE ACCOMPANIMENT OF A TAMBOURINE AND CLAPPERS
Chamba

82 THE FISH INCARNATION OF VISHNU KILLING THE
DEMON HAYAGRIVA From a Vishnu Avatar
series.
Chamba
c. 1740
6⅝ x 10⅜

The god Vishnu, during the course of history,
has been incarnated in many forms (avatars)
to rid the world of demons or demonic
forces. Before assuming the form shown here,
he has been a tortoise and a man-lion. His best
known avatars are Rama (in the *Ramayana*)
and Krishna (in the *Bhagavata Purana* and other
texts). In his fish avatar, he is able to combat
and destroy a river demon. The range of
greens and the unusual compartmentation
of the river are typical of Chamba painting
at this time. For the facial type of the human
portion of the avatar, see Skelton, pl. 47.

82 THE FISH INCARNATION OF VISHNU
KILLING THE DEMON HAYAGRIVA
Chamba
Color plate page 15

83 THE MARRIAGE OF BHARATA AND MANDAVI
From a *Ramayana* series.
Chamba
c. 1755-60
10½ x 14⅝
Ex Coll.: Howard Hodgkin.
The almost savage faces of earlier Chamba
pictures were changing to something less

intense in the years just prior to the date of
this series. The palette of the picture, despite
the prevalence of red, is more subdued.

Leaves from a *Bhagavata Purana* series, bearing
the date, 1757, on one of them, have been
reproduced by Mittal in *Lalit Kala,* no. 12
(1967). In style this *Bhagavata Purana* is very
similar to the present *Ramayana.*

83 THE MARRIAGE OF BHARATA AND MANDAVI
Chamba

The small state of Guler southwest of Kangra played a crucial role in the development of painting in the Punjab Hills. As early as 1703 under Raja Dalip Singh (1695-1741), a local chronicle records artists at the Guler court, and recent research by Dr. B. N. Goswamy has revealed that not only Seu, father of the painters Manaku and Nainsukh (Basohli q.v.), was a native of Guler, but that the family home of their grandfather, Hasnu, was at Guler also. No paintings by these older artists have so far come to light but pictures connected with Dalip Singh show that early painting in Guler tended to employ flat red backgrounds and structures of a geometric nature. A further feature was the constant inclusion of the local landscape in pictures. The fort at Haripur (capital of Guler) stands above the Ban Ganga river on rocky slopes which have the same curving contours noticeable in a famous series, the *Siege of Lanka*. This series was formerly in the Guler Raj collection and is now, in great part, at Boston. Other details which give a local flavor to Guler painting are lakes and rivers abruptly edged by swerving banks, projecting trees, and jutting promontories. What the jungle is to painting in Kotah, the Ban Ganga landscape is to painting in Guler.

In about 1730, Raja Govardhan Chand (reigned 1741-73) began to administer the state for his father, Dalip, and from then onwards Guler painters rapidly adjusted a Muhammad Shah-style of Mughal painting to the serenely sensuous needs of a Rajput court newly influenced by the cult of Krishna. Prior to 1700, religion in Guler had focused on Rama, Shiva, and Durga, but in 1725 missionaries from the Vaishnava center of Damthal in Nurpur founded a new center at Bathu in Guler and encouraged Raja Dalip Singh to erect Krishna temples. Although no great Guler versions of the *Gita Govinda* or the *Bhagavata Purana* are known, many isolated pictures on Krishna themes (no. 85 a) were produced. These vie with studies of ideal lovers, *Ragamalas* (no. 84), palace beauties, and family portraits of the raja as the chief subjects of Guler painting.

Until the late 1760s Guler painters consistently explored the theme of feminine charm, depicting ladies with elegant composure in striking contrast to the contorted figures of Basohli, Mankot, and Kulu. Violence and agitation were excluded, and even in scenes of battle (no. 86), the protagonists were shown moving abstractedly in a dance rather than clashing with purposeful fury. Under Raja Prakash Chand (ruled 1773-90, died 1820), a fresh type of face with straight nose and brow became fashionable and this was continued under his successor Bhup Singh (ruled 1790-1813, died 1823). Earlier features, such as a fondness for red backgrounds and for flatly geometric compositions, were also maintained.

By 1770 patronage at the Guler court appears to have slackened and it was in two other states—its northern neighbor, Kangra (see next section), and Garhwal, a large state at the southeasterly end of the Punjab Hills—that Guler painters found new patronage. The Garhwal royal family had for some time been on close terms with the Guler house, a circumstance illustrated by the employment in Garhwal of Guler nobles as administrators and the occurrence of at least two marriages between Garhwal and Guler families. Shortly before 1770 painters from Guler appear to have arrived at Srinagar, the Garhwal capital, and from then until the occupation of the state by the Gurkhas in 1804, they developed a distinctive Garhwal variant of the Guler manner. The style had the same tranquil grace and serene dignity of painting in Guler, but changes of environment seem to have affected the artists in as forcible a way as Kulu had affected artists from Basohli. The Haripur fort and the Ban Ganga river are replaced by the river Alaknanda—the two hills jutting into the stream—while slender trees with leafless branches, or with great shoots of blunt star-shaped flowers, deep blue skies, and new facial idioms are clear departures from standard Guler practice. At the same time, broad expanses of red, seen especially in hillsides (no. 88) or in the margins of oval-shaped pictures (no. 89), suggest that Guler painters did not entirely abandon their earlier conventions. The upshot was a series of pictures in which the poetic needs of Rajput society in the Punjab Hills found perhaps their most sensitive, romantic, and graceful expression (no. 87).

Between 1804 and 1814 Garhwal was in Gurkha hands, and although painting may not have been wholly extinguished it is likely that faced by the Gurkha threat, Guler painters withdrew. The state's liberation by the British led to the installation of Raja Sudarshan Shah (1816-59) as ruler of Tehri, the northern half of the state, and it was here that the painter Chaitu, great-great-grandson of the Guler artist, Manaku, revived the tradition for a period of fifteen to twenty years.

84 SURMANAND RAGA
Guler

84 SURMANAND RAGA From a *Ragamala* series.
Guler

c. 1760

14 x 9⅜

A Persian inscription in a medallion above this
picture (here purposely covered by the mat)
gives the title of this subject. The miniature
has no doubt been cut down, as the right leg of
the left warrior is broken by the border which
was added later—probably when the picture
was mounted on a late Mughal album page
(also covered by the mat).

A new style for Hill painting, associated with
the state of Guler, will supersede completely
the earlier pictures with their strong primary
colors (nos. 53, 56-61, 70, 76 and 77).
There will be more lyrical delicacy, less
simplicity and strength. The change has been
noticeable in the Basohli *Bhagavata Purana*
series of c. 1760-65 (nos. 55 a and b),
contemporary with this picture.

85 Two unrelated Guler pictures.
a) KRISHNA ACCOSTS A COWGIRL
Guler
c. 1790
$7\frac{1}{4}$ x $4\frac{1}{2}$
b) SHIVA AND PARVATI WITH THE BULL NANDI
Guler
c. 1780
$4\frac{3}{8}$ x $6\frac{1}{2}$

The yellow background of the Krishna episode contrasts with the plain red of the Shiva picture. Shiva is here portrayed with five heads, but the snakes, the third eye in the middle of his forehead, and the ever patient Nandi are already well-known. The red background is a Guler convention that will reappear in Garhwal pictures (see no. 88).

85b SHIVA AND PARVATI
WITH THE BULL NANDI
Guler

85a KRISHNA
ACCOSTS A COWGIRL
Guler

86 THE GODDESS CHANDI (AMBIKA)
ROUTS THE HOST OF THE
DEMON CHIEF DHURMA LOCHANA
Guler

86 THE GODDESS CHANDI (AMBIKA) ROUTS THE
HOST OF THE DEMON CHIEF DHURMA LOCHANA
From a *Makandeya Purana* series.
Guler
c. 1830 (from an earlier original)
7 x 9¼ (within the black border)

The receding bands of the landscape planes
have a completely different feeling from the
separate compartments and registers of early
Rajasthani painting (cf. nos. 3, 5, and 8). Here
they reflect the growing distance toward the
mountains in the background. The lower band
includes the goddess' tiger which leaps upon
the demon host. In the rounded second band,
Chandi sits in front of the fire which will shortly
reduce the demon chief to smoke and ashes.
Two further planes of receding distance occur
on the right, and the whole landscape pattern
is topped, like a cake, by the frosting of
the Himalayan mountain peaks. A certain
"children's book" feeling pervades the picture.
The demons are almost figures of fun. We are
far from the great Pahari masterpieces. (The
black border with its small leaf decoration is
common in late paintings from the Hill States.)

Another leaf from this series is reproduced in
Lee and Archer, no. 54. Still others are in the
Archer and MacDonald collections.

87 RADHA AND KRISHNA ON A HILLTOP
Garhwal
c. 1780-90
8 5/8 x 5 7/8

Nowhere is the calm lyrical beauty of later
Hill painting more evident than in this masterly
oval picture (the mat covers the unfinished
corners which have been damaged by water).
In the background, a pair of cowherds tend
their cattle near a village, a genre scene similar
to certain vistas in early Flemish paintings.
Nothing, however, detracts from the repose of
Krishna who gazes lovingly at his beautiful
Radha. For them, the bower to which they
have retired is far removed from the vulgar
concerns of daily life. Flowering trees have
blossomed just for their delight. A strange
addition, out of place in the perfect foliage, is
the presence of leafless branches, common in
Garhwal pictures (see also nos. 88 and 96).
The excessively long face of Krishna's foster
father Nanda (the worshipper in the lower left)
contrasts with the shorter heads of the
couple. The latter are squat, as though pressure
has been applied under the chin and on top of
the head to press the features forward. The
juxtaposition of these two opposite types of
heads is also found in a miniature reproduced in
Randhawa (1956), pl. 9 and Archer (1957),
pl. 20.

87 RADHA AND KRISHNA
ON A HILLTOP
Garhwal
Color plate page 16

88 KRISHNA VANQUISHES RUKMA
From a *Rukmini Haran* (*the Rape of Rukmini*)
series, an episode in the *Bhagavata Purana*,
11th book.
Garhwal
c. 1790–1800
10¾ x 14¾ (within yellow borders since the
leaf is lacking parts of its outside black border)

88 KRISHNA
VANQUISHES RUKMA
Garhwal

The beautiful Rukmini's marriage to Sisupala
has been arranged. She writes to Krishna to
urge him to save her, and he arrives at the
capital of her royal father. After abducting
Rukmini, he must defeat the demon hosts of
her fiancé. Balarama aids in the fray, and even
after the defeat of Sisupala's army, Rukma,
Rukmini's brother, still continues to fight. He
is shown here about to be captured after his
horses are killed under him. At the pleading of
Rukmini in Krishna's chariot, he will be spared.
The red background, already used by Guler
painters (cf. no. 85 b), is taken up in Garhwal
also. The bare branches that dot the crest of
the mountain in the background have been
mentioned above.

No leaves from this series have so far been
reproduced, but others are in the Binney
collection and in several West Coast private
collections.

89 RADHA AND KRISHNA BESIDE THE COWPEN
From a *Sat Saiya* series.
Garhwal
c. 1790–1800
7¾ x 5⁹⁄₁₆ (within borders)
The oval format of Guler pictures (no. 85 b),
seen again in Garhwal (no. 87), now becomes
widespread. In the 19th century, it will become
common (nos. 91 and 93) with increasingly
complex decoration in the corners, which are
bare here. Another convention, which
will also be used in Kangra painting, is the
daisy-petal form of the foliage on the tree
behind Krishna. It appears also in
nos. 92 b and 94.
Other leaves from this series are reproduced in
Stchoukine, pl. 100; Archer (1954), pl. 8; and
Khandalavala, nos. 200 and 201. Other leaves
are in the MacDonald collection. The
identical episode in another *Sat Saiya* series is
reproduced in Khandalavala, fig. 46.

89 RADHA AND KRISHNA
BESIDE THE COWPEN
Garhwal

KANGRA

While painters in Garhwal were evolving poetic and sensitive variants of the Guler manner, other artists from Guler were producing in Kangra the largest and most famous school of Rajput painting in the Punjab Hills. Until 1770, there is no evidence that Kangra had any local painting. With its vast castle flanked by precipices, the state had early attracted Mughal attention; and from 1626, when the fortress was taken by the Emperor Jahangir, until 1775, when the young Raja Sansar Chand (1775-1823) came to the throne, the state's western part had been controlled by the emperor's deputy, a Mughal Governor. Under Ghamand Chand (1761-73), Kangra had become a greater force, a new castle had been built at Tira Sujanpur on the river Beas, and the state had come to rival in importance Jammu, Chamba, and Bilaspur. Sansar Chand exploited these achievements and in 1786 with Sikh support regained the great castle whose early loss had so weakened Kangra power. From then he gradually assumed the former Mughal Governor's powers, exacted tribute from almost all the southern states and created a court unrivalled for its wealth and proud display of feudal glory. In 1805, dissatisfaction among other states coalesced with an invasion by the Gurkhas of Nepal; Kangra was overrun, and although Sansar Chand was rescued in 1809 by the Sikh Maharaja Ranjit Singh, he ceased to be the overlord of the Hills, lost the Kangra castle, and became tributary to the Sikh "emperor" in the Punjab Plains. From 1809 until his death in 1823, he lived in comparative obscurity at Alampur, Sujanpur, and Nadaun on the river Beas, planning to regain his powers, brooding on his former glory, and maintaining a much dwindled establishment. When the British traveller, Moorcroft, visited him in 1820, he was impressed on three accounts—the Raja's delight in dancing girls, his devotion to Krishna, and his "fondness for drawing." Moorcroft noted that he possessed many hundred of pictures and that he still employed several artists.

This interest in painting, combined with his rise to power and sudden wealth, may explain the abrupt movement of painters to Kangra. Between 1775 and 1806 two styles of Kangra painting are apparent. The first is a journalistic record of court events focusing chiefly on Sansar Chand and his brother, Fateh Chand. Of no great sensitivity, this style is partly reflected in a Krishna subject (no. 91) where the border can be paralleled in certain portraits. The second style is a serenely graceful development from Guler painting of the 1760 to 1775 period and is largely devoted to studies of the Krishna theme. At least three artists from Guler are known to have taken part. Khushala, second son of Manaku (the Guler painter who executed the 1730 *Gita Govinda* at Basohli), is named by oral tradition as Sansar Chand's favorite painter. Gaudhu, second son of Nainsukh, also of Guler, was jealously regarded by a newcomer as monopolizing patronage—the latter's grievance finding expression in a personal letter to Sansar Chand. Purkhu, yet a third native of Guler, was represented posthumously at a Fine Arts Exhibition in Lahore in 1864 and was noted as being formerly "in the service of Raja Sansar Chand" and as displaying "remarkable clearness of tone and delicacy of handling."

Apart from a huge variety of unrelated individual pictures, the greatest achievements of Kangra painting between 1775 and 1805 are four great series—a *Bhagavata Purana* (where Purkhu's qualities are strikingly apparent), a *Gita Govinda* and parts of a *Sat Saiya* (in which Khushala and Gaudhu may possibly have collaborated) and a *Ragamala* (perhaps the work of later Guler arrivals). Change of court, locality, and patron must clearly have provided a potent stimulus, and in all these works important new developments are present. A greater premium is put on spontaneity of gesture, effortless naturalism, and on figures in motion. Geometric structures are replaced by more relaxed compositions. In place of the rocky hills of Guler and the sharp bends of the Ban Ganga, settings reflect the gently undulating meadows, tranquil slopes, and placid stream of the river Beas at Alampur. Above all, respect for Sansar Chand's devotion to Krishna endows the style with passionate nobility, making romance itself appear an almost religious rite. Although no examples from these great sets are included in this exhibition, a flavor of their style can be obtained from no. 90 a-c.

Following the hiatus in painting involved by the Gurkha invasion and Sansar Chand's eclipse, Kangra painting entered a new phase in 1809. A *Nala Damayanti* series, depicting the adventures of a prince who loses his kingdom but, in the end, regains it, was probably prepared in the years 1809 to 1814, perhaps serving as an allegory of Sansar Chand's career and an augury for its happy conclusion. The first part, fully painted and complete, is now in the Karan Singh collection, Jammu; examples of the second part, still in the drawing stage, have for long been a glory of the Boston Museum. In these pictures, the later Guler face with straight nose and forehead has become more evident, but the style has still a supple fluency, delicately expressive of poetic exaltation.

Between 1820 and 1825, a second *Gita Govinda* (no. 92 a-b) and a *Rasika Priya* (no. 93) were probably produced—the former perhaps in celebration of a wedding. In both sets the early romantic feeling remains, but the manner has now become harsher and harder. Following the abdication of Sansar Chand's son, Anirudh, in 1828, Kangra was annexed by the Sikhs and in 1849 was converted into a British district. A coarse *Bhagavata Purana* (no. 94) painted somewhat later but based on a version of about 1785, illustrates how dependent on Sansar Chand had been Kangra painting in its finest period.

90b A MAN HANGING FROM
A TREE WITH THREE CROWS
Kangra

90a VISHNU AND
LAKSHMI SEATED
ON A LOTUS
Kangra

90 Three leaves from an unidentified series.
   c. 1790
   4 3/8 x 3 5/8
   a) VISHNU AND LAKSHMI
      SEATED ON A LOTUS
      Numbered, in *nagari* characters, "12."
   b) A MAN HANGING FROM A TREE WITH
      THREE CROWS
      Similarly numbered, "18."
   c) A DRUMMER BEATING ON TWO KETTLE DRUMS
      Similarly numbered, "67."

The mature style of the state of Kangra is
heralded by these three little illustrations to an
unidentified series. The typical profiles of the
school are those of the god and goddess of 90 a.
The sophistication of the painted portions of
each little square belies their unfinished look.

Another single leaf from this series has been
reproduced in Craven, no. 66. It is from the
Bickford collection and must be one of many
leaves from the series. It bears the number "53"
in *nagari* characters.

90c A DRUMMER BEATING
ON TWO KETTLE DRUMS
Kangra

91 RADHA GOES AT NIGHT TO KRISHNA'S HOUSE
From a *Rasika Priya* series.

c. 1805

11⅝ x 9⅜

Ex Coll.: Howard Hodgkin.

The use of a vertical oval frame for miniatures is a late development in Pahari painting. (It hardly occurs at all in Rajasthani works.) The earliest example in this exhibition is the Garhwal picture of Radha and Krishna (no. 87) of c. 1780. (The Guler example, no. 85 b, is a horizontal oval which is much less prevalent.) From that period on, oval miniatures become increasingly common, particularly in *Ragamala* and *Rasika Priya* series. The triangular decoration in the corner spaces helps establish different parts of the same set and contemporary works.

91 RADHA GOES AT NIGHT
TO KRISHNA'S HOUSE
Kangra

92a KRISHNA BEGS
A FRIEND OF RADHA
TO PRESENT HIS CASE
TO HER AND
TO INDUCE HER
TO RETURN TO HIM
Kangra

92 Two leaves from the "Lambagraon" *Gita
Govinda* series.
c. 1820–25
11 1/16 x 14 3/16
Ex Coll.: Raja Dhruv Dev Chand of
Lambagraon, Kangra, Punjab Hills.

a) KRISHNA BEGS A FRIEND OF RADHA TO
PRESENT HIS CASE TO HER AND TO INDUCE
HER TO RETURN TO HIM

b) KRISHNA AWAITS ANXIOUSLY TO HEAR OF THE
SUCCESS OF HIS EMISSARY TO RADHA

Radha and Krishna have quarreled. His
go-between fails to bring about a reconciliation
(92a), so he must try a second time sending

the same friend (92b).

The lyrical beauty of the great Kangra masterpieces are well illustrated here in the great delicacy of color and complexity of rhythm. In 92a the separation of the lovers is accomplished. The birds in the trees sit singly. The forest is more sparse, the sky more open. Leaf 92b presupposes the re-establishment of the broken union; birds appear in pairs, tree trunks in the center and right side of the picture are girdled with flowering vines.

Other leaves from this series have been reproduced in French, pl. 22; and Khandalavala, no. 263.

92b KRISHNA AWAITS ANXIOUSLY TO HEAR OF THE SUCCESS OF HIS EMISSARY TO RADHA
Kangra
Color plate page 17

93 A FRIEND TRIES TO CONSOLE THE LONELY RADHA
From a *Rasika Priya* series.

c. 1820-25

12⁷⁄₁₆ x 8¾

Inscription above the picture reads: *radhika ko prasang bitanbas.*

Radha's wait for Krishna has been in vain, and her friend attempts to divert her attention. The bright, delicate intensity of the bedroom is contrasted with the blackness of the night sky where it is almost impossible to see the pair of peafowl and the rain clouds.

Leaves from this series have been reproduced in Khandalavala, nos. 247, 264, 266; and in Randhawa (1962), fig. 19. Other leaves are in the Victoria and Albert Museum, London.

93 A FRIEND TRIES
TO CONSOLE
THE LONELY RADHA
Kangra

94 KRISHNA KILLS THE CRANE DEMON BAKASURA
From a *Bhagavata Purana* series.
c. 1850 or later
$11\frac{5}{8}$ x $13\frac{5}{8}$

Bakasura, the crane demon, has terrorized the
cattle and cowherd boys of Brindaban.
Krishna defeats him by allowing the giant
bird to swallow him (left) and then swelling
up to split the crane's beak (right).
Later Kangra painting unsuccessfully tries to
continue the production of its early years.
A brittle hardness and stereotyped pattern
become increasingly obvious. In this miniature
the composition is very similar to pictures from
earlier *Bhagavata Puranas,* but the disquieting
green colors betray the decadence of the style.
For the prototype of this miniature, from a
Kangra series of c. 1780, see Randhawa
(1960), pl. VI.

JAMMU AND HINDUR

Like Kangra, Jammu was at one time a powerful state in the Punjab Hills. Painting, however, flourished there for less than a century—its greatest period being from 1745 to 1760, when the Guler painter, Nainsukh, worked for the Jammu prince, Balvant Singh. Nainsukh's work was in many ways outside the main stream, but his family connection with Guler may explain the presence of Guler-type female figures in Jammu pictures of the years 1775 to 1790. In a portrait of Raja Brij Raj Dev (ruled 1781-87), the attending ladies exactly resemble Draupadi, the central figure of no. 95 b.

Hindur (also known as Nalagarh from the name of its capital) lies south of Bilaspur

95 Two leaves from similar *Bhagavata Purana* series.
Jammu
c. 1780-1790

a) KRISHNA AND BALARAMA RIDE FORTH TO ATTEND THE PROCLAMATION OF YUDISTHIRA AS A "WORLD RULER."

$10\frac{3}{8}$ x $14\frac{1}{2}$ (within borders)

Exhibited: Persian and Indian Miniatures, Binney collection, Portland Supplementary Exhibition, Cat. no. 88 b.

Yudisthira, leader of the Pandavas, announces his claim to the title of "Ruler of the World" at a great sacrifice which precedes a feast. Krishna and Balarama ride in their chariots to attend the celebrations. At the feast, the Kauravas, rivals of the Pandavas, gamble with their host. Yudisthira's continuous losses result in his losing his kingdom, his brothers, and finally his wife Draupadi whom he shares with his brothers in polyandrous marriage.

b) THE UNVEILING OF DRAUPADI

10 x $14\frac{1}{4}$ (within borders)

Draupadi is presented to the durbar presided over by the blind king Dhritarashtra, leader of her Kaurava captors. When one of them attempts to remove her clothes forcibly, she prays to Krishna as Vishnu to spare her this ignominy. Her prayers are answered, and, as soon as one covering is snatched away, another takes its place and she remains continuously veiled, regardless of how often the process is repeated. Here she stands demurely before the lecherous glances of the Kauravas, the pile of clothes growing around her feet as the frustrated Kaurava, Duryodhana, continues to try to overcome the divine intervention.

These two leaves are almost consecutive illustrations to the epic. They are contemporary among the stony hills which adjoin the Punjab Plains. Until the 19th century it had little painting, but between 1810 and 1820 it developed a local style based on late painting at Bilaspur. Krishna viewing the cowgirls (no. 96) is in the same style as a Hindur variant of a famous Bilaspur picture of Krishna fluting to the cattle (Archer [1960], pl. 74). A feature of Hindur painting in the first half of the 19th century is delight in frothy flowering trees—a detail seen to advantage in no. 97. The somewhat glib harshness of this latter picture may be due to Sikh influence from the Punjab plains. The Sikhs had become the paramount power in the Punjab Hills in 1810 and remained so until their final defeat by the British in 1849. Paintings of the Sikhs (1830-50) have at times a boisterous virility which is in strong contrast to the gentle smoothness of painting in Guler and Kangra.

95b THE UNVEILING
OF DRAUPADI
Jammu

and both exhibit characteristics of the style of Jammu. Both were purchased from the same Sotheby auction (February 1, 1960). The measurements of the picture surface, however, are dissimilar, and the borders are of different colors (95a is dark blue; 95b is the more usual red). It is possible that they come from different *Bhagavata Purana* series though painted at approximately the same time.

One leaf from the same or a similar series is reproduced in Welch and Beach, no. 54, and in Beach (1965), pl. 7. Other leaves are in the Royal Scottish Museum, the Victoria and Albert Museum, the Fogg Art Museum, and in the Archer, MacDonald, and Yeon collections.

96 KRISHNA REGARDS THE COWGIRLS ACROSS
A LOTUS POOL
From a *Bhagavata Purana* series.
Hindur
c. 1810-20
11⅛ x 13½

The divine cowherd and his friends regard
one another with mutual wonder across the
open forest glade beside the lotus-filled pool.
Again we find the horizontal bands or registers
which we have seen previously, particularly
in nos. 48, 72, and 86; but now they are more
subtle in their presentation. In the foreground
the pond with its profusion of lotus is extended
into the next higher register with the lozenge
shape of its farthest portion. The band of
grass, surrounding the clumps of flowers and
the human figures, merges easily into the
barrier of trees because of the intervention of
the strip of tree trunks. High above, the empty
sky is broken only by bare spears and dead
tree branches. Everywhere these registers are
broken but continue to exist.

96 KRISHNA
REGARDS
THE COWGIRLS
ACROSS A
LOTUS POOL
Hindur

97 KRISHNA AND BALARAMA EMBRACE AFTER THE
DEFEAT OF THE SNAKE DEMON KALIYA
From a *Bhagavata Purana* series.
Hindur
c. 1850-60
11½ x 15⅝

One of the youthful exploits of Krishna was
the *Kaliya Damana,* the quelling of a huge
water snake which terrorized the banks of the
Jamuna by his predatory behavior and his
poisonous exhalations. Krishna leaped into the
river to wrestle with him and only spared
Kaliya after his snake-wives had pleaded for
his life. He promised to go into exile and to
leave the region in peace. Here, while Krishna
is congratulated by his half brother, the coils
of the demon snake unwind, and he and his
wives swim away.
It is significant that, although considerably
later in date than no. 96, the picture employs
the same distinctive color range—orange,
white and blue-black in the dresses, white and
orange-red for the cascading sprays of flowers.

97 KRISHNA
AND BALARAMA
EMBRACE AFTER
THE DEFEAT
OF THE SNAKE
DEMON KALIYA
Hindur

Sculpture and Weapons

SCULPTURE

A SHIVA. FRAGMENT OF A STATUE, TORSO AND
HEAD. Black schist. Idar (Gujarat)
c. 8th century

H. 20

Shiva is depicted with four arms. The
lower right is broken off; the upper right
holds a trident, common attribute of the
god; his left lower arm grasps a weapon
across his body; and the upper left arm
holds an attribute which has been so
severely abraded that it is unrecognizable.
Idar, in West India, north of Bombay,
produced sculpture which is close to the
great heads and bas-reliefs of the Caves
of Elephanta in Bombay harbor. Few
examples of the contemporary sculpture
of this part of India exist outside of India
itself; and the Museum in Baroda, close
to the Idar region, has one of the few
strong collections even in India.

B VISHAWASENA, STEWARD OF VISHNU'S
HOUSEHOLD (or Vishnu himself), WITH
ATTENDANT DEITIES Cream sandstone.
Base of a temple pillar. Border of
Rajasthan and Central India.
10th century

H. 24

The conch shell, one of the most usual
attributes of Vishnu, stands above the
figures. It no doubt belonged to a much
larger statue of the god which towered
over his devotees.
Despite the abrasion of the whole group,
which must have formed the base of a
large column on the outside of a temple,
a sinuous, lyrical quality is evident here
which places this group in diametric
opposition to the similar group, no. C,
which is roughly contemporaneous with it.

C A FEMALE DEITY, WITH TWO MALE
ATTENDANTS, STANDS BEHIND A SMALL
BUDDHA AND A KNEELING DEVOTEE.
Cream sandstone.
Rajasthan
10th – 11th century

H. 20

This fragment, less abraded than no. B
above, shows none of its swaying
musicality. Again, the loss of portions of
this group of worshippers makes
identification impossible.

D A RAMPANT LION, WITH A FALCON HEAD.
Pink sandstone.
Temple decoration from Khajuraho.
11th – 12th century

H. 26

Khajuraho, a series of temples in
Bundelkhand (Central India) is well known
as a tourist mecca. This fragment was no
doubt removed from the side of one of
the temples at the time when Indians first
discovered the value of their artistic
heritage and rushed to dismember their
ancient religious buildings. Since an Indian
shrine seldom exhibited many free-standing
figures, the pillagers despoiled the carved
decorations which were a notable part of
the architecture.

WEAPONS

E KATAR (stabbing dagger with blade which
opens upon another, fixed, blade).
Rajput or Mughal
18th – 19th century

L. 16¾

This kind of weapon can be seen, in the
belts of many of the men pictured in the
miniatures of the exhibition (see nos. 3,
5, 10, 12, 27, 56a-b, 63, 66, 70b, 82, 83,
94b). It is a warrior's weapon, and is
almost never worn by the gods, even in

Continued

their terrestrial manifestations. The user squeezed the two horizontal bars in the middle of the handle; the blade then opened to inflict a more horrible wound than the usual deep cut. This "ripping apart" rather than simple stabbing was necessary in charges of elephants. When the beasts had overrun the positions of foot soldiers and were directly above them, the men could counter-attack against the bellies of the elephants.

F DAGGER WITH CARVED JADE HANDLE AND BLADE DECORATED WITH GILDED ARABESQUES
Rajput or Mughal
18th - 19th century
L. (of handle) 5
L. (of blade) 12¼
The use of carved jade, originally a

Chinese monopoly, became increasingly common in India. At first in particular demand by the Mughals, jade also became common in the hilts of Rajput weapons.

G DAGGER WITH JADE HILT SET WITH TURQUOISES AND RUBIES
Silver sheath set with diamonds at the forte. Late 18th or early 19th century.
L. (of blade) 14¼
W. (of handle) 5½
The *tau* form (like the Greek letter "T") is peculiar to the Punjab, but was no doubt seen in the Pahari states during the Sikh occupation. Such a weapon, with its heavy incrustation of semi-precious gems and over-elegant scabbard, was a parade piece and was not used for war. Its razor-sharp point made it no less lethal.

H CURVED SWORD WITH ENAMELLED LION'S HEAD ON THE POMMEL.
Rajput
18th - 19th century
L. (of hilt) 6¾
L. (of blade) 30
The scimitar shape of this sword suggests an Islamic provenance. The curved blade was also common in India. The enamelled work on the handle, the tip of the scabbard, and the two bands which helped in suspending the weapon from a warrior's waist, are more typically Rajput. Compare the caparison of Raja Ram Singh of Jodhpur (no. 33) who sports not one, but two, similar weapons. The under one, whose scabbard lies farthest up on the rump of his mount, is very similar to this, but without the distinctive pommel.

Abbreviations of Works frequently cited in the Catalog

ARCHER, *Bundi and Kotah*
  Archer, W. G. *Indian Painting in Bundi and Kotah*. London, 1959.
ARCHER, *Indian Miniatures*
  Archer, W. G. *Indian Miniatures*. London and New York, 1960.
CHANDRA, *Bundi*
  Chandra, P. *Bundi Painting*. New Delhi, 1959.
CHANDRA, *Mewar*
  Chandra, M. *Mewar Painting in the Seventeenth Century*. New Delhi, 1957.
HEERAMANECK CATALOG
  Beach, M. C. "Rajput and Related Paintings," *The Arts of India and Nepal: the Alice and Nasli Heeramaneck Collection*. Museum of Fine Arts, Boston, 1966.
KANORIA CATALOG
  Archer, W. G. *Indian Paintings from Rajasthan*. London, 1957.
KHAJANCHI CATALOG
  Khandalavala, K., Chandra, M., and Chandra, P. *Miniature Paintings from the Sri Motichand Khajanchi Collection*. New Delhi, 1960.
KHANDALAVALA
  Khandalavala, K. *Pahari Miniature Painting*. Bombay, 1958
LEE
  Lee, S. E. *Rajput Painting*. New York, 1960.

MC NEAR CATALOG
  McNear, E. and A. *Indian and Persian Miniatures from the Collection of Everett and Ann McNear*. Chicago, n.d.

Other bibliographical references will be by the author's name and the year of publication. In those few cases where two works were published by a single author in the same year, the first work listed in the bibliography will have the letter "a" added to the year of publication, the second work the letter "b." Where a single work by an author is listed, the author's name alone will suffice.

N.B. The reference, "Persian and Indian Miniatures, Binney Collection, West Coast Tour, 1962-63," is to an exhibition organized by the Portland Art Museum, which, after showing there, was exhibited at the following museums: Tacoma Art Museum, Tacoma, Washington; Stanford University Art Gallery and Museum; Salt Lake Art Center, Salt Lake City, Utah; Fine Arts Gallery of San Diego; Seattle Art Museum; Pasadena Art Museum; Museum of Art, Eugene, Oregon; Oakland Art Museum; Art Gallery of Greater Victoria, Victoria, B.C.; Vancouver Art Gallery, Vancouver, B.C.; Colorado Springs Fine Arts Center. The catalog of this exhibition is listed in the bibliography under "Binney." A supplementary exhibition of related works from the Binney Collection was shown at Portland only.

Bibliography

ARCHER, MILDRED

    Indian Miniatures and Folk Paintings. London, 1967.

ARCHER, MILDRED AND W. G.

    Romance and Poetry in Indian Painting. Wildenstein, London, 1965.

ARCHER, W. G.

    Indian Painting in the Punjab Hills. London, 1952.

    Kangra Painting. London and New York, 1952; revised 1956.

    Garhwal Painting. London and New York, 1954; revised 1957.

    "Some Nurpur Paintings," *Marg,* VIII, no. 3 (1955), 8-18.

    Indian Painting. London, 1956.

    "The Problems of Painting in the Punjab Hills," *Marg,* X, no. 2 (1957), 30-36.

    Indian Paintings from Rajasthan. (A catalogue of the G. K. Kanoria Exhibition, Arts Council of Great Britain). London, 1957.

    The Loves of Krishna. London and New York, 1957.

    Central Indian Painting. London and New York, 1958.

    Indian Painting in Bundi and Kotah. London, 1959.

    Indian Miniatures. London and New York, 1960.

    "Review of E. Dickinson and K. Khandalavala: *Kishangarh Painting,*" *Lalit Kala,* no. 6 (dated 1959, but published 1961), 82-88; and no. 8 (dated 1960, but published 1962), 75-77.

    Foreword to M. S. Randhawa, *Kangra Paintings of the Gita Govinda.* New Delhi, 1963.

    Paintings of the Sikhs. London, 1967.

ARCHER, W. G. AND BHATTACHARYA, D.

    Love Songs of Vidyapati. London, 1963.

ASHTON, SIR L. (edit.)

    The Art of India and Pakistan. London, 1950.

BARRETT, D. AND GRAY, B.

    Painting of India. London, 1963.

BEACH, M. C.

    "A Bhagavata Purana from the Punjab Hills," *Bulletin, Museum of Fine Arts, Boston,* LXIII, no. 333 (1965), 168-177.

    "Rajput and Related Paintings," *The Arts of India and Nepal: the Alice and Nasli Heeramaneck Collection.* Museum of Fine Arts, Boston, 1966.

BINNEY, E.

    Persian and Indian Miniatures from the Collection of Edwin Binney, 3rd. Portland Art Museum, Portland, Oregon, 1962.

CHANDRA, M.

    Mewar Painting in the Seventeenth Century. New Delhi, 1957.

    "Paintings from an Illustrated Version of the *Ramayana* Painted at Udaipur in A.D. 1649," *Bulletin of the Prince of Wales Museum,* Bombay, no. 5 (1957), 33-40.

CHANDRA, M. AND MEHTA, N. C.

    The Golden Flute. New Delhi, 1962.

CHANDRA, P.

    "A Ragamala Set of the Mewar School in the National Museum of India," *Lalit Kala,* nos. 3 and 4 (dated 1956-57, but published 1958), 46-54.

    "An Outline of Early Rajasthani Painting," *Marg,* XI, no. 2 (1958), 32-37.

    Bundi Painting. New Delhi, 1959.

COOMARASWAMY, A. K.

    Rajput Painting. Oxford, 1916.

    Catalog of the Indian Collections in the Museum of Fine Arts, Boston, Part V, Rajput Painting. Cambridge, Massachusetts, 1926.

CRAVEN, R. C.

    Miniatures and Small Sculptures from India. University of Florida, Gainesville, 1966.

DICKINSON, E. AND KHANDALAVALA, K.

    Kishangarh Painting. New Delhi, 1959.

EASTMAN, A. C.

    The Nala Damayanti Drawings. Boston, 1959.

FRENCH, J. C.

    Himalayan Art. Oxford, 1931.

GHOSE, A.

    "The Basohli School of Rajput Painting," *Rupam,* no. 37
    (1929), 6-17.

    "Pahari Schools of Indian Painting," *Roopa Lekha,* XXVIII,
    nos. 1 and 2 (1958), 34-44.

GOSWAMY, B. N.

    "The Pahari Artists," *Roopa Lekha,* XXXII, no. 2 (1961), 31-50.

    "Golu, the Nurpur Artist," *Marg,* XVII, no. 3 (1964), 62.

    "Painting in Chamba: A Study of New Documents," *The Asian
    Review,* II, no. 2 (1965), 53-58.

    "Re-readings of some 'Takri' Inscriptions in Khandalavala's
    Pahari Miniature Painting," *Roopa Lekha,* XXXV, nos. 1 and 2
    (1966), 69-75.

    "The Artist-Family of Rajol: New Light on an Old Problem,"
    Roopa Lekha, XXXV, nos. 1 and 2 (1966), 15-23.

    "The Problem of the Artist Nainsukh of Jasrota," *Artibus Asiae,*
    XXVIII (1966), 205-210.

    "A Painter's Letter to his Royal Patron," *Journal, American
    Oriental Society,* LXXXVI, no. 2 (1966), 209-216.

GRAY, B.

    "Western Indian Painting in the Sixteenth Century: The Origins
    of the Rajput School," *Burlington Magazine,* XC, no. 539
    (February, 1948), 41-49.

    Rajput Painting. London and New York, 1948.

    "Painting," *The Art of India and Pakistan* (Sir L. Ashton, ed.).
    London, 1950.

    "The Development of Painting in India in the 16th Century,"
    Marg, VI, no. 3 (1953), 19-24.

HAJEK, L.

    Miniatures from the East. Prague and London, 1960.

HENDLEY, T. H.

    The Rulers of India and the Chiefs of Rajputana, 1550-1897.
    London, 1897.

KANORIA, G. K.

    "An Early Dated Rajasthani *Ragamala,*" *Journal, Indian Society of
    Oriental Art,* XIX (dated 1952-53, but published 1957), 1-5.

KHANDALAVALA, K.

    "Leaves from Rajasthan," *Marg,* IV, no. 3 (1950), 2-24, 49-56.

    "A *Gita Govinda* Series in the Prince of Wales Museum,"
    Bulletin of the Prince of Wales Museum, Bombay, no. 4 (1954), 1-18.

    "The Origin and Development of Rajasthani Painting,"
    Marg, XI, no. 3 (1958), 4-17.

    Pahari Miniature Painting. Bombay, 1958.

KHANDALAVALA, K. AND CHANDRA, M.

    "The *Rasamanjari* in Basohli Painting," *Lalit Kala,* nos. 3 and 4
    (dated 1956-57, but published 1958), 26-38.

    "Three New Documents of Indian Painting," *Bulletin of the
    Prince of Wales Museum, Bombay,* no. 7 (1959-62), 23-34.

    "An Illustrated Manuscript of the *Aranyaka Parvan* in the
    Collection of the Asiatic Society, Bombay," *Journal, Asiatic
    Society of Bombay,* XXXVIII (dated 1963, but published 1964),
    116-121.

KHANDALAVALA, K., CHANDRA, M. AND CHANDRA, P.

    Miniature Paintings from the Sri Motichand Khajanchi Collection.
    New Delhi, 1960.

KHANDALAVALA, K., CHANDRA, P. AND DAS, P.

    "A New Document of Indian Painting," *Lalit Kala,* no. 10
    (dated 1961, but published 1963), 45-54.

KRISHNA, A.

    "Some Pre-Akbari Examples of Rajasthani Painting," *Marg,* XI,
    no. 3 (1958), 18-21.

KRISHNADASA, RAI.

    "An Illustrated Avadhi Mss. of *Laur Chanda,*" *Lalit Kala,*
    nos. 1 and 2 (1955-56), 66-71.

LEE, S. E.

    Rajput Painting. New York, 1960.

    A History of Far Eastern Art. London and New York, 1964.

LEE, S. E., ARCHER, MILDRED AND ARCHER, W. G.

    Indian Miniatures from the Mildred and W. G. Archer Collection.
    Smithsonian Institution, Washington, 1963.

LEE, S. E. AND CHANDRA, P.

    "A Newly Discovered *Tutinama* and the Continuity of the Indian
    Tradition of Manuscript Painting," *Burlington Magazine,* CV,
    no. 729 (December, 1963), 547-554.

MC GREGOR, J. R.

Indian Miniature Paintings from West Coast Private Collections.
M. H. De Young Memorial Museum, San Francisco, 1964.

MC NEAR, E. AND MC NEAR, A.

*Indian and Persian Miniatures from the Collection of Everett and
Ann McNear.* Chicago, n.d.

MEHTA, N. C.

Studies in Indian Painting. Bombay, 1926.

MITTAL, J.

"Some Ramayana and Bhagwata Drawings of Chamba," *Marg,*
VIII, no. 3 (1955), 26-31.

"An Illustrated Manuscript of Madhu Malati and Other Paintings
from Kulu," *Lalit Kala,* nos. 3 and 4 (dated 1956-57, but
published 1958), 90-95.

"An Early Guler Painting," *Lalit Kala,* no. 11 (dated 1962, but
published 1965), 31-34.

"New Studies in Pahari Painting," *Lalit Kala,* no. 12 (dated
1963, but published 1967), 26-35.

RANDHAWA, M. S.

"Guler, the Birthplace of Kangra Art," *Marg,* VI, no. 4 (1953),
30-44.

Kangra Valley Painting. New Delhi, 1954.

"Paintings from Nalagarh," *Lalit Kala,* nos. 1 and 2 (1955-56),
81-86.

The Krishna Legend in Pahari Painting. New Delhi, 1956.

"Kangra Artists," *Roopa Lekha,* XXVII, no. 1 (1956), 4-10.

Basohli Painting. New Delhi, 1959.

Kangra Paintings of the Bhagavata Purana. New Delhi, 1960.

"A Note on *Rasamanjari* Paintings from Basohli," *Roopa Lekha,*
XXXI, no. 1 (1960), 16-26.

"Paintings from Mankot," *Lalit Kala,* no. 6 (dated 1959, but
published 1961), 72-75.

Kangra Paintings on Love. New Delhi, 1962.

Kangra Paintings of the Gita Govinda. New Delhi, 1963.

"Some Portraits of Rajas of Basohli in Kangra Style," *Roopa
Lekha,* XXXIV, nos. 1 and 2 (1965), 5-9.

Chamba Painting. New Delhi, 1967.

RAWSON, P. S.

Indian Painting. London, 1962.

REIFF, R.

Indian Miniatures: the Rajput Painters. Rutland, Vermont, 1959.

SASTRI, H.

Indian Pictorial Art as Developed in Book-Illustration. Baroda, 1936.

STCHOUKINE, I.

La Peinture indienne à l'époque des grands Moghols. Paris, 1929.

SKELTON, R.

Indian Miniatures from the XVth to XIXth Centuries. Venice, 1961.

TOD, J.

Annals and Antiquities of Rajasthan. London, 1829; re-issued
Oxford, 1920, ed. W. Crooke.

WALDSCHMIDT, E. AND WALDSCHMIDT, R.

Musikinspirierte Miniaturen. Wiesbaden, 1966.

WELCH, S. C.

The Art of Mughal India. New York, 1963.

WELCH, S. C. AND BEACH, M. C.

Gods, Thrones and Peacocks. New York, 1965.

STAFF OF THE EXHIBITION

Dr. Francis J. Newton, *Director*

Rachael Griffin, *Curator*

Donald Jenkins, *Curatorial Assistant*

Pauline Eyerly, *Education and Publicity*

Robert Peirce, *Librarian*

CREDITS

Design, Lynch and Van Cleve Associates

Photography, Alfred A. Monner

Set in Monotype Bembo, Paul O. Giesey-Adcrafters

Printed in U.S.A. at Graphic Arts Center,

Portland, Oregon